THE MICROCIRCULATION

THE MICROCIRCULATION

Symposium on
Factors Influencing Exchange of Substances
Across Capillary Wall

Edited by

S. R. M. REYNOLDS, Chairman, Fifth Microcirculatory Conference; Professor and Head, Department of Anatomy, University of Illinois College of Medicine

BENJAMIN W. ZWEIFACH, Secretary-Treasurer; Professor of Pathology, New York University—Bellevue Medical Center

Proceedings of the Fifth Conference on Microcirculatory Physiology and Pathology, Buffalo, New York, April 1, 1958

THE UNIVERSITY OF ILLINOIS PRESS

Urbana, 1959

PREFACE

The Fifth Microcirculatory Conference was held in Buffalo, New York, on April 1, 1958, in conjunction with the annual meeting of the American Association of Anatomists. It convened to fulfill once again the objectives of the Conference in order to bring together research workers from diverse fields to consider their common interests with regard to the minute blood vessels of the body.

With this end in view, half a day was devoted to a symposium on the subject of "Factors Influencing Exchange of Substances Across Capillary Wall." In this were brought together outstanding minds in areas of the ultrastructure of the capillary wall, the forces of a functional character that appear to operate in and about minute vessels, and the functional capabilities of artificially made protein-bearing membranes with micropores. The recorded text of the symposium and the comments and questions elicited bear testimony to the fact that there is as yet no common basis upon which the anatomist and physiologist may explain the mechanism or mechanisms by which substances pass into or out of blood capillaries. If, in defining the limits of their respective positions, the discussants have drawn their lines clearly for all to see, they will have served a most useful purpose. Someone, somewhere, may see the way or ways that the gap between anatomists and physiologists may be bridged. With this in mind, attention of readers is directed to all the comments of Dr. Arnold.

In addition to the planned symposium, half a day was given over to an open forum for the delivery and discussion of seven presentations. These are wide-ranging in interest and are a token of the interest of those individuals who make up the membership of the Conference. Provocative ideas are to be found in these presentations. For this reason they are included in this volume as part of the transactions of the day, even though some are to be published elsewhere.

This volume is the fifth of the Conference series to be published. The first, "Technics for the Microscopic Study of Small Blood Vessels and Blood Flow," was published in *Anatomical Record*, 120:241-361, 1954. The second, "Vascular Patterns as Related to Functions," was published in *Angiology*, 6:281-413, 1955. The third, "Factors Regulating Blood Flow," was published as a separate volume by the *American Physiological Society* in 1958. The fourth conference, "Tissue Reactions to Injury," is in process of publication. It is hoped in the future that a central place of publication will attract increasing attention to the proceedings of these Conferences and so make them more readily available and more widely appreciated.

The beginning of the Fifth Conference took place in Chicago in November, 1957, when the Executive Committee, under the chairmanship of Dr. R. H. Ebert, met to discuss plans for the next year. Dr. Benjamin W. Zweifach, continuing as the Secretary-Treasurer, has been the common denominator to the recent Microcirculatory Conferences, giving from his experience and wisdom the benefit of his advice. Others on the Committee were Drs. G. P. Fulton, E. H. Block, John W. Irwin, A. G. Sanders, and E. P. Fowler, with the writer present as Chairman-elect. Without the advice of this committee the symposium presented at Buffalo could not have been as it was, stimulating for those present. To the members of the Executive Committee I give my thanks. Sincere appreciation is likewise expressed to the U. S. Public Health Service for a substantial sustaining contribution (Grant H-2662) and to the twelve pharmaceutical companies whose support means so much. These are listed at the end of this volume. This support provides especially for the social and some of the conference expenses that are incidental to the growing success of these Conferences; the Public Health Service grant supports some of the basic costs of running the Conference and aids in the publication of these Transactions. Participants, of course, provide for their own support and transportation to the Conference. All in all, an effective synthesis seems to have been achieved by individuals, by private industry, and by a government agency to create annually an environment for the exchange of ideas across several disciplines having broad areas of interest which, in the normal course of events, might never take place under such effective and stimulating situations.

S. R. M. REYNOLDS

CONTENTS

Tuesday Afternoon Session
April 1, 1958

The session convened at two o'clock, Dr. S. R. M. Reynolds presiding.

CHAIRMAN REYNOLDS: A panel was assembled last winter in pursuance of the decision of the Executive Committee to hold a symposium today on the subject of capillary permeability. In planning this, it seemed that there were several kinds of approaches that ought to be considered.

We needed to know what the anatomists could tell us of the structure of the tissues with which we are concerned; we needed to know something of the physiological conditions to which these structures are subjected; and, finally, we needed to know, in so far as they would help us to understand the problem, what experimental models have to reveal in terms of exchange of fluids and molecules of various sizes. And so, with this in mind, as your chairman, I solicited the good offices of the people whom you see here. What will come out of it I cannot say. The program is unrehearsed and unprepared. I think that it is going to be profitable for you to hear these people. We have asked each one to talk for a half-hour to forty-five minutes. Then we are going to have two invited discussants to start things going. They will say whatever they care to say and then we will have discussion from the floor.

I am going to call for the first presentation of the afternoon, Dr. Don Fawcett of Cornell University Medical College, who very graciously accepted, after a little needling and insistence on my part, to talk about "The Fine Structure of Capillaries, Arterioles and Small Arteries."

THE FINE STRUCTURE OF CAPILLARIES, ARTERIOLES AND SMALL ARTERIES

Don W. Fawcett

Cornell University Medical College

My assignment in this symposium is to review the traditional concept of the structure of small blood vessels and to present some of the changes that have come about as a result of the use of the electron microscope. The problem is to relate, in so far as possible, the physiological measurements of capillary permeability to the structure of the vessel wall. Until a few years ago we believed that if we could obtain more magnification and a little better resolution than was afforded by the light microscope, the problem of the mechanism of exchange across the capillary wall would be solved. This expectation has certainly not been borne out. The greatly increased resolution provided by the electron microscope has, in fact, complicated the problem, and in some respects morphologists and physiologists are farther apart in their interpretations today than they were a decade ago.

As a point of departure, let us consider the architecture of the capillary wall as it was visualized ten years ago when Chambers and Zweifach(3) published their splendid review on capillary permeability (Fig. 1). Identifying the successive layers of the capillary wall from the lumen outward, there was first the so-called *endocapillary layer,* which was believed to be an adsorbed layer of some protein constituent of blood plasma. Next there was the *endothelium,* composed of living and nonliving portions. The living part, the *endothelial cells,* comprised the greater part of the surface of the wall, and the non-living portion, the *intercellular cement,* made up a relatively small fraction of the surface and was believed to consist of a porous material, possibly a calcium proteinate. Preparations in which the endothelial cell boundaries were impregnated with silver gave the impression that there was an appreciable amount of this intercellular cement, and there was experimental evidence indicating that its physical state could be modified by varying the pH or the calcium content of a perfusate. The idea of a capillary basement membrane analogous to that of other epithelia had been dismissed as unlikely

This study was supported in part by a grant from the Life Insurance Research Fund.

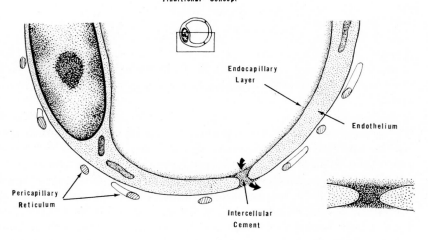

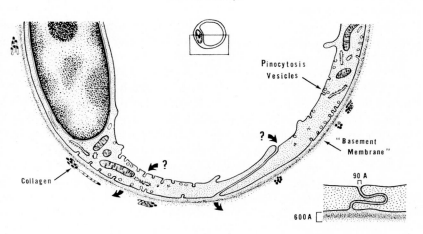

Figs. 1 and 2.

by Krogh and Vimtrup(8) but was still accepted by some investigators. All seemed to agree that there was a *pericapillary sheath*, consisting of a closely woven investing layer of argyrophilic connective tissue fibers. It was the prevailing opinion that capillary permeability depended primarily upon the non-living intercellular cement, the cells serving to form the wall of the vessel and to elaborate and maintain the intercellular substance. The "cement" was thought to act as an ultrafilter whose selective properties depended upon variations in its porosity. This formulation of the morphological basis of capillary permeability seemed to fit most of the available physiological data, and it gained widespread acceptance.

In 1953, Pappenheimer(15) after carrying out meticulous gravimetric studies of capillary exchange in perfused limbs of cats, arrived at conclusions that were not fundamentally different from those of Chambers and Zweifach(3) in 1947, namely, that the passage of water and water-soluble molecules takes place through channels or pores penetrating the capillary wall. The total cross-sectional area of the pores seemed to comprise less than 0.2 per cent of the histological surface of the capillaries. Thus, it was thought that these hypothetical pores might well be limited to the area between the endothelial cells. The measured rates of passage across the capillary wall could be accounted for by assuming the presence of pores 30 to 50 Å in diameter in the intercellular substance. On the other hand, it was believed that all or the greater part of the endothelial cell surface was available for passage of lipid-soluble molecules, oxygen, carbon dioxide, and other substances that are soluble in lipid as well as in water.

ELECTRON MICROSCOPY OF CAPILLARIES

From this brief résumé of morphological observations with the light microscope and the inferences drawn from physiological measurements, we now turn to a review of the finer structure of capillaries as revealed by our own electron microscopic investigations and similar studies already published from several other laboratories—Palade(12); Policard *et al.*(17); Kisch(6, 7); Moore and Ruska(11). Depending upon its size and the level of section, the capillary wall may be formed of one endothelial cell rolled up with its edges cohering or it may be made up of segments of two, three, or four cells. In the small capillary shown in Fig. 3 the entire circumference consists of a single endothelial cell enclosing a lumen that is completely occluded by an erythrocyte which, by chance, is oriented transversely. The endothelial cell membrane and the outer limit of the erythrocyte are both clearly defined and the two are separated in some places by no more than 100 Å. This close apposition of the surfaces does not leave room for an endocapillary layer of any appreciable thickness. Moreover, in other figures (Figs. 4, 8, and 9) no adsorbed

layer of protein can be seen coating the exposed surface of the endothelium. It is concluded from these findings that the postulated endocapillary
layer either does not exist or is not preserved by current methods of
specimen preparation. The free surface of the endothelium is usually
smooth or undulant but occasionally there are a few slender villi that
project a short distance into the blood stream. These have been referred
to by Kisch(6, 7) as "tentacles," a term that implies prehensile properties
which these microvilli probably do not possess. They do not seem to be
common enough to be a functionally significant feature of capillary structure.

The endothelial cells possess all of the usual cell organelles, but show
no structural specializations that can be definitely related to transport
across the capillary wall. The flattened nucleus is generally elliptical in section and often shows infoldings and other irregularities of its outline (Figs.
3 and 15). As in many other cells of mesenchymal origin, the nuclear
boundary is particularly prominent, owing to the presence of a dense
granular layer of uniform thickness closely applied to the inner aspect
of the membrane (Figs. 1 and 14). The nucleolus is compact in its organization and shows no unusual features. The remainder of the karyo-
plasm is quite homogeneous in well-fixed specimens (Fig. 14). A small
Golgi complex and a pair of centrioles are found near the nucleus. The
mitochondria, which are not particularly abundant, are located for the
most part in the perinuclear region, but also occur in the more attenuated
peripheral portion of the cell. The small number of the mitochondria and
their relatively simple internal structure suggest that the energy requirement for normal endothelial cell function is not high. The endoplasmic
reticulum is represented by a few vesicular and elongated profiles with
granules of ribonucleoprotein associated with their limiting membrane.
Other free granules of the same nature are distributed throughout the
cell. The cytoplasmic matrix of the endothelial cell has a fine filamentous
component that is not illustrated in the relatively low power electron
micrographs presented here. The filaments may either be randomly
oriented and widely dispersed or may be concentrated in definite fibrous
tracts in the cytoplasm. Palade(12) described fibrils in endothelial cells,
but other investigators have failed to find them(17). In favorable preparations we find them consistently but estimate their thickness to be less
than 100 Å instead of 240 Å as stated by Palade. In electron micrographs
of arterioles and small arteries the fine filaments are often present in
greater abundance in the endothelium than they are in the cytoplasm
of the neighboring smooth muscle cells. The filaments in both are of about
the same thickness and density. The question arises as to whether they
have similar contractile properties in both. Numerous experimental
studies have established that capillaries change their caliber by passive

distention and elastic recoil, but many workers also believe they are capable of active contraction. Some have attributed this property to special *adventitial cells* or *pericytes*(8), but others have reported contraction of capillaries on which no adventitial cells could be seen(5). Most of these observations, however, have been made on amphibia. In mammals there is very little evidence that the adventitial cells contract, and the power of contractility of the endothelial cells is generally believed to be so limited that they probably play no significant role in the control of the circulation(19). The finding of tracts of oriented filaments in electron micrographs of endothelium is consistent with the belief that these cells may have considerable contractile powers of their own.

On the outer surface of the capillary is a 500 to 600 Å layer of amorphous-appearing material that corresponds to the basement membrane of other epithelia. Within this layer there is often a noticeable variation in density with a light zone being found immediately adjacent to the endothelial cell membrane and a darker zone about 400 Å away from it. Peripheral to this, the layer again diminishes in density so that its exact outer limit is poorly defined (Figs. 3, 8, and 9). Although this basement membrane usually appears amorphous, high resolution electron micrographs reveal that it consists of a feltwork of exceedingly fine filaments embedded in a homogeneous matrix(23). Its strong histochemical staining reaction for 1–2 glycol linkages suggests that one of its major components is mucopolysaccharide. In this respect it is like the ground substance of common connective tissue, but the two are clearly different in their solubility. The basement membrane is preserved by osmium fixation, whereas the connective tissue ground substance does not persist through the usual steps in preparation of tissue for electron microscopy. Contrary to prevailing opinion, the basement membrane does not seem to be merely a condensation of the surrounding ground substance, but is more likely a product of the endothelial cells themselves.

In capillaries of the renal glomerulus which have a discontinuous endothelium, it is the continuous basement membrane rather than the cellular portion of the wall which appears to be the barrier controlling the composition of the glomerular filtrate. There can be little doubt that this layer is an important factor in determining the permeability of other capillaries as well. One of the most pressing histophysiological problems is the need for a better understanding of the chemical nature and physical properties of this important tissue component.

The ability to elaborate this relatively stable mucopolysaccharide appears to be a property of many cell types. A coating of this substance is not peculiar to the basal surface of epithelia, but is also found on the sarcolemma of skeletal and cardiac muscle, smooth muscle, Schwann cells, and on other cell types of mesenchymal origin. The presence of an extraneous coating of this kind may have a more important part than is generally realized in determining the permeability of the cell surface to substances present in the extracellular fluid.

A perivascular reticulum is poorly developed on the capillaries of human cardiac muscle (Figs. 3 and 4), but on those of other organs (Fig. 14), scattered small bundles of collagen fibrils are associated with the outer aspect of the basement membrane. Pericytes are common and are indistinguishable from endothelial cells in their fine structure (Figs. 3, 8, and 14). They too are surrounded by a layer of mucopolysaccharide which blends with the basement membrane of the endothelium.

Traditional theories of capillary permeability have depended heavily upon the existence of an appreciable intercellular space between endothelial cells occupied by a permeable cement substance (Fig. 1). The recent observations with the electron microscope do not provide the support for this concept that was expected. The cells occasionally meet in simple edge-to-edge relationship with a short surface of contact, but more commonly the thin margins of the endothelial cells overlap for a distance of 0.5 to 1.0 μ (Figs. 2 and 3). Frequently the opposing cell surfaces show a deep intercrescence so that, in sections, the configuration of the boundary recalls the familiar tongue-in-groove, or mortise-and-tenon joints of the cabinet-maker (Figs. 4 and 5). The lengthening of the intercellular pathway that results from either imbrication or interdigitation of the cell surfaces would not favor the free passage of substances through the wall. Instead, the complexity of the boundaries suggests that this is a means of increasing the area of contact to insure a firmer union between the endothelial cells. The distance between the opposing cell membranes at the junctions between endothelial cells is remarkably small, ranging from 90 to 150 Å. The interspace is occupied by material of the same appearance and density as that at the base of the endothelial cells, and it is quite probable that the intercellular material is of essentially the same chemical nature as the mucopolysaccharide substance comprising the capillary basement membrane. The exceedingly narrow intercellular gap is only two or three times the theoretical pore size calculated by Pappenheimer and if it is, in fact, the principal avenue for egress of fluid and water-soluble molecules, the area available for this exchange probably represents a smaller percentage of the total surface of the capillary wall than was thought to be the case from older observations made with the light microscope on preparations in which silver had presumably been deposited in the "intercellular cement."

To date there has been no morphological demonstration in electron micrographs of the passage of material between endothelial cells, and the dimensions of the intercellular clefts make it somewhat unlikely that

these could account for a major part of capillary exchange. Nevertheless, experimental evidence indicating that this is an important pathway
continues to accumulate(10), and it has been shown for other epithelia
involved in transport that particulate matter can pass between cells.
During absorption of lipid by the intestinal mucosa, for example, it has
been found that lipid is taken into the cell in small droplets of rather
uniform size. A considerable number of these are subsequently discharged into the cleft between adjacent epithelial cells, from whence
they pass into the interstitial spaces of the lamina propria(14). In the
kidney of frogs injected with thorotrast, small amounts of thorium dioxide
pass into the glomerular filtrate, are then taken up by the epithelium of
the tubules, and are found (Fig. 10) between the interdigitated surface
of adjacent cells(21). Dense granules of unknown chemical nature normally occur in the epithelial cells of the nephron of the horned lizard,
Phrynosoma, and these same granules accumulate in high concentration
in the intercellular clefts (Fig. 11) and between the cells and the basement membrane(1). In electron micrographs of the fresh-water polyp,
Hydra, particles believed to be glycogen are found between the cells of
the ectoderm (Figs. 12 and 13), and there is evidence that it is transported intercellularly and that it traverses the mesogloea, a layer which
corresponds to the basement membranes of higher metazoa(20). It is
well known that leucocytes migrate through many normal epithelia, penetrating the basement membrane and insinuating themselves between the
membranes of neighboring cells. After their passage, the cell surfaces
re-establish their intimate contact. It is apparent, therefore, that whatever may be the nature of the intercellular substance or of the physical
forces which normally maintain the cohesion of cells, there is a potential
space between cells which is permeable under certain conditions to colloidal particles, lipid droplets, particulate cell products, and even to leucocytes. Thus, notwithstanding the close approximation of the endothelial
cells revealed in electron micrographs, it is not unreasonable to believe
that the intercellular pathway may be importantly involved in transport
of fluid and ions across the capillary wall. At the present time we know
so little about the physicochemical laws which apply to the movement
of molecules between lipoprotein membranes 100 Å apart, that it profits
us little to speculate as to how the cell surfaces can be firmly held a
constant distance apart and how, at the same time, a free and rapid
flow of molecules might be maintained in the intervening space in a
direction parallel to the confronted membranes. The techniques being
developed by Dr. Arnold for production of model films having dimensions and microstructure similar to those of biological membranes promise
to tell us much about the purely physical factors involved in passage of
fluid and ions through small interstices, but there will still remain to

be elucidated those additional factors related to the specific chemical properties of plasma membranes and of the intercellular substance.

We turn our attention now to another possible mechanism of transport. In proposing the "intercellular cement" as the probable site of capillary exchange, Chambers and Zweifach(3) commented, "The alternative to this is the unlikely occurrence of active uptake by cells through a complex process of phagocytosis on an ultramicroscopic scale." Recent electron microscopic findings have made this alternative far less "unlikely" today than it seemed to be in 1947. Micrographs of capillaries show numerous inpocketings of the endothelial plasma membranes. Some of these communicate by a narrow neck with the lumen of the vessel, others form small closed vesicles immediately beneath the cell membrane (Figs. 2, 6, 8 and 9). Minute vesicles of this kind are often seen along the basal, as well as the luminal, surface of the endothelial cells. Such vesicles were first described by Palade(12), who interpreted them as evidence of a submicroscopic order of pinocytosis and suggested that they might play a role in the active transport of substances across the capillary wall. It was thought that fluid might be taken into vesicles on the luminal surface, and that these might migrate across the cell to the basal surface where they would release their contents into the pericapillary interstitial fluid. Moore and Ruska(11), in a recent study of capillaries, strongly support this thesis and propose a new term to describe this kind of cellular activity. It is suggested that *pinocytosis* be used to describe the active incorporation of fluid by cells for their own use, but that a new term *cytopempsis* be applied to the taking up of fluid into small vesicles for transport across the cell. Several considerations stand in the way of easy acceptance of this attractive hypothesis. Among these is the intracellular distribution of the so-called "transport vesicles." As a rule, they are present in considerable numbers at both the luminal and basal membranes of the endothelial cells, but relatively few are seen in the intervening cytoplasm. To account for the paucity of vesicles in the cell body, it would have to be argued that the time required for them to migrate across the cell is short compared to the time consumed either in their formation at the one surface or their discharge at the other. The only alternative to this explanation would require that the vesicles be formed anew near the surface at which they are assumed to be discharged. Efforts to demonstrate the participation of such vesicles in the transport of colloidal particles across capillary endothelial cells have met with limited success. Wissig(22) obtained inconclusive results with thorium dioxide and colloidal mercuric sulfide, but found that ferritin injected into the blood stream passed through the endothelium and basement membrane of muscle capillaries. In electron micrographs some of the particles could be seen in transit. They appeared to enter the cells by being incorporated in pinocytosis vesicles, but they also seemed to be able to penetrate the membrane directly. Vesicles containing particles were seldom seen along the base of the endothelial cells. These findings establish that material which traverses the capillary wall enters the endothelial cells, but they do not provide a clear-cut demonstration that the vesicles observed are a major vehicle of fluid transport. If capillary exchange were an active process dependent upon vesiculation of the cell membrane, one would expect this kind of surface activity to be peculiar to the capillary endothelium, or at least more highly developed there than in other tissues. Such is not the case. Minute vesicles of exactly the same kind are associated with the plasma membrane of mesothelial cells, fibroblasts, smooth muscle cells, and cardiac muscle fibers. Indeed, in the walls of arterioles and small arteries these vesicles are often considerably more abundant in the smooth muscle cells of the media than they are in the endothelium. In view of the widespread occurrence of membrane vesiculation in cell types not involved in fluid transport, it seems likely that this phenomenon is to be regarded simply as pinocytosis occurring at a submicroscopic level. Although this process is undoubtedly of great importance to cells as a means of taking up fluid in bulk from their environment, it may not be an important mechanism for transport across the capillary wall.

ARTERIOLES AND SMALL ARTERIES

A discussion of the fine structure of vessels larger than capillaries may not seem germane to the subject of this symposium, but it can be defended on the basis that some of the same factors which are operative in capillary exchange are no doubt involved in the nutrition of the walls of those blood vessels which are not provided with vasa vasorum. In arterioles and small arteries the endothelium has a conspicuous basement membrane which blends with the similar mucopolysaccharide coating of the subjacent smooth muscle to form a thick layer separating the intima from the media (Figs. 15 and 16). This amorphous material also extends between the individual muscle cells and around the periphery of the muscle layer. Embedded in this abundant intercellular substance are small bundles of collagen fibrils which correspond to the *reticular fibers* that are seen with the light microscope in silver-stained histological sections of such vessels. It is of interest to note that the individual collagen fibrils comprising the argyrophilic reticulum of the media have a diameter only about half that of the unit fibrils in the "collagenous fibers" of the adventitia (Figs. 18, 20, and 21). It remains unsettled as to whether the argyrophilia characteristic of the fibrils in the media depends upon their smaller size, a different surface charge, or their special relation to the surrounding matrix.

Pinocytosis vesicles are extraordinarily abundant in the smooth muscle cells. One may infer from this that the intercellular matrix does not constitute a significant barrier to the passage of solutes from the lumen into the vessel wall. From a functional standpoint, a large amount of matrix covering most of the surface of the muscle cells may be advantageous in permitting limited shearing movements of one surface over the other as the cells change shape in contraction. On the other hand, a closer union between cells at certain points is probably a mechanical necessity if their contraction is to be effective in altering the caliber of the vessel. Furthermore, if the cells were separated at all points by a thick layer of intercellular substance this would, no doubt, interfere with the spread of the contractile process throughout the muscle layer. It is probably significant, therefore, that at certain points on the surface of the muscle cells one or more blunt processes project through the intercellular matrix and make intimate contact with the surface of the neighboring cells (Fig. 19). These areas of closer contact appear to correspond to the structures in ureteral smooth muscle which Bergman(2) referred to as "intercellular bridges." Here in the walls of blood vessels they are relatively few and variable in size. There is no evidence of protoplasmic continuity between cells, nor is there any thickening or other visible specialization of the apposed cell membranes. Thus the term "intercellular bridge" does not seem appropriate even though it is likely that these are physiologically important contacts between cells.

Electron micrographs confirm the histological observation that the elastin of small arteries forms a discontinuous layer composed of longitudinally oriented, parallel strands situated between the endothelium and the muscle coat. In cross-sections these strands appear as uniformly spaced, rounded areas that are slightly more dense than the surrounding intercellular matrix (Fig. 17). It was not appreciated with the light microscope how closely the base of the endothelial cells conforms to the irregular corrugated surface presented by the elastica. The cells are separated from it only by a thin "basement membrane" and they send finlike processes deep into the slits between adjacent strands of elastin (Fig. 17). As reported by Moore and Ruska(11) the cell processes sometimes extend all the way through these narrow fenestrations and make contact with the underlying smooth muscle cells. A continuous layer of elastin might be relatively impervious; thus the existence of fenestrations in the elastica may serve to keep pathways open for exchange of metabolites between the blood and the vessel wall.

The elastin generally appears dense and homogeneous after osmium fixation, but occasionally in very thin sections it appears to be composed of fine filaments embedded in an abundant amorphous matrix, a structure which is in accord with previous descriptions by Rhodin and Dalhamm(18) of elastin in the lamina propria of the trachea and by Dettmer(4) of elastin in the ligamentum nuchae. The filaments are straight and parallel and more slender than the finest recognizable unit fibrils of collagen. No evidence is found to substantiate the report by Lansing *et al.*(9) that elastic tissue is made up of helically coiled strands. The elastin and the surrounding amorphous intercellular substance have very nearly the same opacity to electrons and there is some indication that the two components are being confused. For example, the statement by Moore and Ruska(11) that the material of "the elastica interna continues without sharp borderline between adjacent smooth muscle cells" is not supported by our experience either with light or electron microscopy and may be based upon a confusion of elastin with the subendothelial amorphous matrix which does continue without interruption between the smooth muscle cells (Fig. 15). In human vessels dense granular deposits are occasionally found within the elastin (Fig. 17). These do not appear to be normal constituents of the elastica and probably represent early pathological changes. An unexpected finding is the very intimate association of the elastin and collagen. Small bundles of collagen fibrils are often partially or completely incorporated in the heavy bands of elastic tissue, a relationship which raises interesting problems concerning the mode of formation of these two different connective tissue components.

Whether cellular or local mechanical factors are more important in determining the type and disposition of fibers is entirely unknown, but as Pease and his co-workers(16) have recently pointed out, the precursors of both the collagen and elastin must be formed by endothelium or smooth muscle or both, for no other cell type is present in the vessel wall.

SUMMARY

We have discussed the submicroscopic structure of capillaries in relation to traditional theories of transfer through the capillary wall. The possibilities given most careful consideration were: (1) that substances leave the capillaries between cells, passing through submicroscopic pores in the intercellular substance; (2) that they are actively transported through the cells by a process of pinocytosis wherein fluid is taken into small vesicles at the luminal surface and is liberated into the perivascular tissue fluid at the endothelial cell base.

Electron microscopic observations have provided little support for the concept of intercellular pores currently favored by physiologists. The space between cells has been found to be much narrower than was believed to be the case, and no pores have been seen in the intercellular substance. Injected colloidal particles that pass through the capillary wall have not been observed between endothelial cells even though particulate matter has been found to accumulate intercellularly in other epithelia engaged in transport.

The concept of active transport through the cells, an alternative considered unlikely by most physiologists, has derived unexpected support from electron microscopy. The numerous submicroscopic vesicles associated with endothelial cell membranes do strongly suggest transport by a process akin to pinocytosis. However, efforts to demonstrate the incorporation of intravenously injected particles into these vesicles have given disappointing results. Moreover, the occurrence of such vesicles in several other cell types raises doubts as to their significance in relation to the problem of transport across the capillary wall.

Finally, certain structural features of arterioles and small arteries have been described which may have a bearing upon the nutrition of the tunica media, the spread of the contractile process during vasomotor activity, and the origin of the collagen and elastin of the vessel wall.

REFERENCES

1. Anderson, E. A cytological study of the proximal convoluted tubules of the kidney of the horned toad Phrynosoma cornutum by electron microscopy. Anat. Rec. *130:*449 (abstract) (1958).
2. Bergman, R. A. "Intercellular bridges and conduction in ureteral smooth muscle," *Proc. First European Conf. on Electron Microscopy*. Stockholm, 1956.
3. Chambers, R., and B. W. Zweifach. Intercellular cement and capillary permeability. Physiol. Rev. *27:*431-63 (1947).
4. Dettmer, N. Elektronenmikroskopisch Untersuchungen am elastischen Fasersystem des Ligamentum nuchae. Zeitschr. f. Zellforsch. 265-79 (1956).
5. Federighi, H. Blood vessels of annelids. Proc. Nat. Acad. Sc. *13:*639-41 (1927).
6. Kisch, B. Elektronmikroskopische Untersuchung des Herzens und der Kapillaren. Dtsch. med. Wschr. *17:*605-6 (1957).
7. Kisch, B. Der ultramicroscopische Bau der Capillarwand. Acta physiol. pharm. néerl. *6:*334-38 (1957).
8. Krogh, A., and B. Vimtrup, "The Capillaries," in *Special Cytology*, ed. E. V. Cowdry. New York: Paul B. Hoeber, 1932.
9. Lansing, A. I., and T. B. Rosenthall, M. Alex, and E. W. Dempsey. The structure and chemical characterization of elastic fibers as revealed by elastase and electron microscopy. Anat. Rec. *114:*555-76 (1952).
10. Mende, T. J., and E. L. Chambers. Studies on solute transfer in vascular endothelium. J. Biophys. & Biochem. Cytol. *4:*319-22 (1958).
11. Moore, D. H., and H. Ruska. The fine structure of capillaries and small arteries. J. Biophys. & Biochem. Cytol. *3:*457-62 (1957).
12. Palade, G. E. Fine structure of blood capillaries. J. Appl. Physiol. *24:* 1424 (1953).
13. Palade, G. E. The endoplasmic reticulum. J. Biophys. & Biochem. Cytol. *2:*(supplement) 85-98 (1956).
14. Palay, S., and S. Karlin. Figs. 24-26, in Maximow and Bloom, *Textbook of Histology*, 7th ed.; Philadelphia: W. B. Saunders, 1957.

15. Pappenheimer, J. R. Passage of molecules through capillary walls. Physiol. Rev. 33:387-423 (1953).
16. Pease, D. C., S. Molinari, and T. Kershaw. An electron microscope study of larger intracranial blood vessels of cats and dogs. Anat. Rec. 130:355 (abstract) (1958).
17. Policard, A., A. Collet, and S. Pregermain. Etude au microscope electroniques des capillares pulmonaires. Acta anat. 30:624-38 (1957).
18. Rhodin, J., and T. Dalhamm. Electron microscopy of collagen and elastin in the lamina propria of the tracheal mucosa of the rat. Exp. Cell. Res. 2:295-98 (1955).
19. Sandison, J. C. Contraction of blood vessels and observations on circulation in transparent chambers in rabbit ears. Anat. Rec. 54:105-27 (1932).
20. Slautterback, D. L., and D. W. Fawcett. The development of the cnidoblasts of hydra, an electron microscope study of cell differentiation. J. Biophys. & Biochem. Cytol. 5:441-52.
21. Taylor, J. C. A review of the fine structure of the nephron with some observations on the localization of particulate matter in the nephron. Thesis for the master's degree, submitted to the Graduate School of Cornell University, 1956.
22. Wissig, S. L. An electron microscope study of the permeability of capillaries in muscle. Anat. Rec. 130:467 (abstract) (1958).
23. Yamada, E. The fine structure of the renal glomerulus of the mouse. J. Biophys. and Biochem. Cytol. 1:551-66 (1955).

CHAIRMAN REYNOLDS: Thank you, Dr. Fawcett. We are very much obliged to you for presenting the morphological basis upon which any physiologist or biophysicist, it seems to me, must base his concepts.

With this as a background, we are going to pass on, then, to the second paper of the symposium, which is going to be presented to you by a student of Dr. Pappenheimer, about whom Dr. Fawcett spoke. Dr. Eugene Renkin of the Department of Physiology of the George Washington University School of Medicine is going to talk on "Capillary Permeability and Transcapillary Exchange in Relation to Molecular Size."

Plate I

Fig. 3. A capillary from human heart muscle. The lumen is completely filled by an erythrocyte. The nucleus (Ncl) is somewhat irregular in outline. Mitochondria (M) and a small Golgi complex (GC) are located in the juxtanuclear cytoplasm. Elongated profiles of the endoplasmic reticulum and numerous small vesicles are found throughout the cytoplasm. The thinned-out peripheral portions of the cell overlap (at the arrow) to close the endothelial tube. The capillary is surrounded by a layer of amorphous material forming the basement membrane (BM). A portion of a pericyte (Pc) appears at the top of the figure.

Fig. 4. A capillary from the human myocardium. The lumen is occupied by a fine precipitate of blood plasma. The cell junction (at the arrow) illustrates a common form of interdigitation of the opposing cell surfaces. Numerous small pinocytosis vesicles are associated with both the luminal and basal surface of the endothelium. The basement membrane of the capillary is identical to the amorphous layer investing the sarcolemma of the neighboring cardiac muscle fibers (Mf).

14

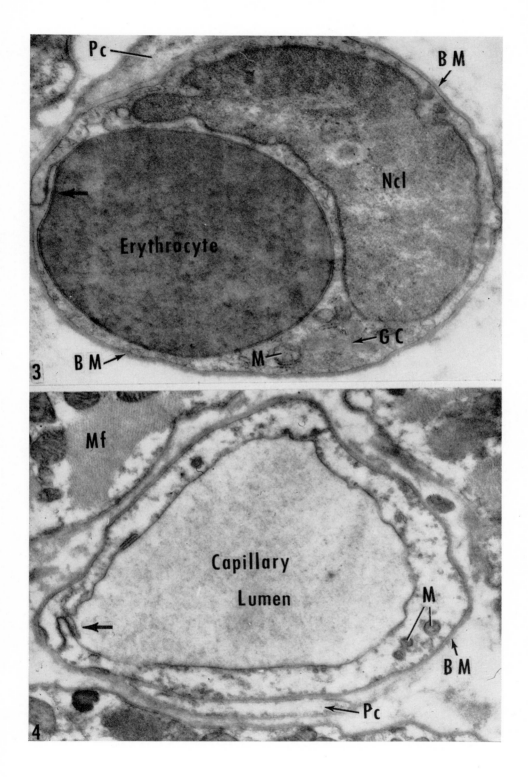

Plate II

Fig. 5. A capillary of the myocardium at higher magnification. The dense ovoid object at the upper left is an erythrocyte in the lumen (Er). No adsorbed endo-capillary layer is visible between the erythrocyte and the endothelial cell membrane. The arrow indicates a typical interlocking cell junction.

Fig. 6. A portion of a myocardial capillary showing an abundance of small vesicles associated with both the luminal and basal surfaces of the cell and also occurring free in the cytoplasm. The vesicles at the endothelial cell surfaces are often open to the capillary lumen or to the basement membrane (see those indicated by arrows).

Fig. 7. A portion of the wall of a capillary illustrating the extreme thinness of the endothelium and the imbrication of the cell margins. The intercellular gap indicated by the arrow is only about 100 Å wide. Note also that if an "endocapillary layer" coating the interior of the vessel exists, it is of low density and exceedingly thin, for the surface of the erythrocyte in the lumen here is separated from the endothelial cell membrane by less than 100Å in some places.

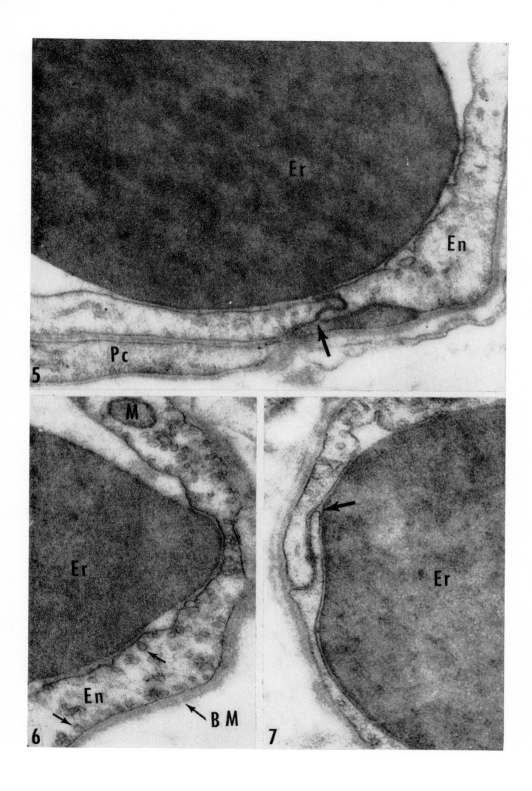

Plate III

Fig. 8. A muscle capillary showing, in the endothelium (En), many small vesicles of the kind that have been interpreted by some investigators as "transport vesicles" and assigned an important role in transcapillary exchange. A small bundle of collagen fibrils (Cl) is associated with the conspicuous basement membrane (BM).

Fig. 9. A portion of capillary wall adjacent to a cardiac muscle fiber. Notice that pinocytosis vesicles are associated with the sarcolemma (Sl) of the muscle fiber (Mf) as well as with the membranes of the endothelial cell (En). Observe also the similarity between the capillary basement membrane (BM) and the extracellular, amorphous component of the sarcolemma.

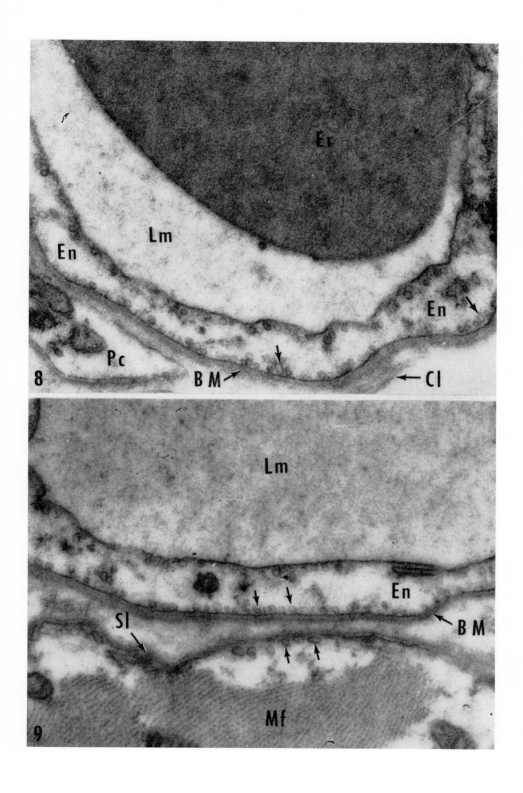

Plate IV

Fig. 10. A portion of the boundary between two epithelial cells in the distal convoluted tubule of frog kidney. The animal had been injected with thorotrast. Thorium dioxide particles have been taken up by the cells in small vesicles and later deposited between the membranes of adjacent cells (arrows). This micrograph is presented to illustrate the point that the intracellular space may be utilized in an epithelium which is active in transport.

Fig. 11. The boundary between two epithelial cells in the nephron of the horned lizard, showing a striking accumulation of granular material of unknown composition between the cells. Some of the granules appear to be within the substance of the basement membrane.

Fig. 12. A small area from the ectoderm of hydra. Between the cells are many small granules believed to be a particulate form of glycogen. (Courtesy of Dr. David Slautterback, Department of Anatomy, Cornell University Medical College.)

Fig. 13. Another micrograph of hydra illustrating the utilization of the intercellular spaces for transport of particulate material (glycogen). (Courtesy of Dr. David Slautterback, Department of Anatomy, Cornell University Medical College.)

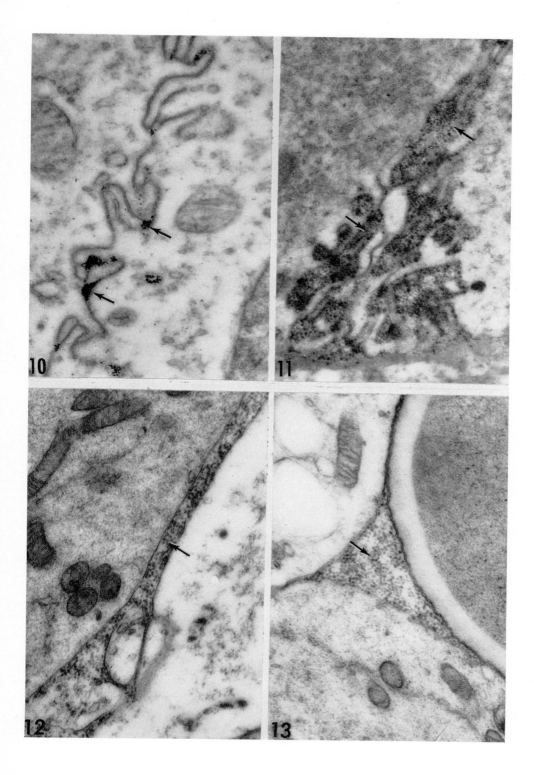

Plate V

Fig. 14. A larger capillary from the interstitium of the human testis. Sections of five endothelial cells (En) make up its wall. Parts of two or more pericytes (Pc) are shown and there is an abundant pericapillary reticulum (Cl).

Fig. 15. A portion of the wall of an arteriole. The endothelial cell (En) above, bulging into the lumen, shows a nucleus (Ncl) of highly irregular shape. Between the endothelium and the muscularis is a thick layer of amorphous matrix (Bm) representing the basement membrane of the endothelium, combined with the corresponding extraneous coating of the underlying smooth muscle cells. This intercellular substance extends between the muscle cells. No elastin is identifiable. (Courtesy of Dr. Alphonso Martinez, Instituto de Neurocirurgía, Santiago, Chile.)

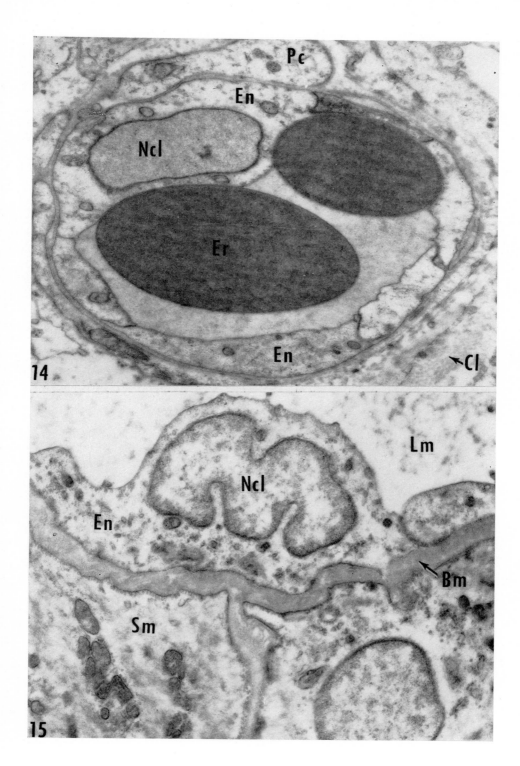

Plate VI

Fig. 16. A segment of the wall of an arteriole. The lumen is at the upper right. Two endothelial cells meet (at the arrow) in a relatively simple, straight junction. The basement membrane of the endothelium and the corresponding layer around the smooth muscle cells (Sm) are united to form a single rather thick layer between endothelium and the muscular coat (Bm). Numerous small vesicles are seen in the endothelial cytoplasm and along the outer membrane of the smooth muscle cells.

Fig. 17. An area from the wall of a small artery from the human testis. The lumen (Lm) and endothelium (En) are shown, above, and a smooth muscle cell (Sm) at the bottom of the figure. Between these are cross-sections of several longitudinally oriented bars of elastin (El) forming a discontinuous elastica interna. Observe that the basal surface of the endothelium closely conforms to the irregular surface upon which it rests, sending finlike processes deep into the narrow fenestrations in the elastica (at arrows). Between the endothelium and the elastin is a thin continuous layer of basement membrane material. Dense granular deposits in the elastin appear to represent early pathological changes.

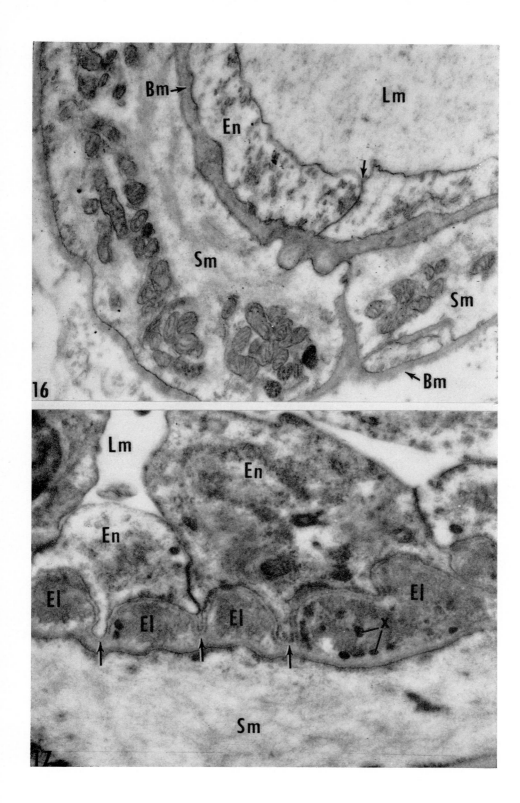

Plate VII

Fig. 18. A longitudinal section through the wall of a small artery from the human testis. At the top of the figure is the lumen (Lm) containing erythrocytes (Er). Moving downward one finds, in turn, the endothelium (En), the smooth muscle (Sm), and at the bottom of the figure a portion of the adventitia. Certain areas of particular interest (rectangles A, B, and C) are shown at higher magnification in Figs. 19, 20, and 21.

Fig. 19. The smooth muscle cells of the media are, for the most part, surrounded by a thick layer of intercellular matrix. At certain places, however, blunt processes of the cell (at arrow) project through this material to come into more intimate contact with the surface of the adjacent cell. It is likely that these areas of closer contact are essential to transmit the pull of one cell upon another and to permit propagation of the impulse to contract throughout the muscular layer. (For orientation see rectangle A in Fig. 18.)

Fig. 20. Embedded in the intercellular matrix are bundles of collagen fibrils which correspond to the "reticular fibers" of light microscopy. It is of interest that the unit fibrils within these bundles are only about half the diameter of those comprising the collagen fibrils of the adventitia. Compare the size of the retouched fibril encircled with one in Fig. 21 which was photographed at the same magnification. (For orientation of Fig. 20, see rectangle B in Fig. 18.)

Fig. 21. Circumferentially oriented collagen fibrils from the adventitia are shown here in cross-section for comparison with those in Fig. 21 (see rectangle C in Fig. 18).

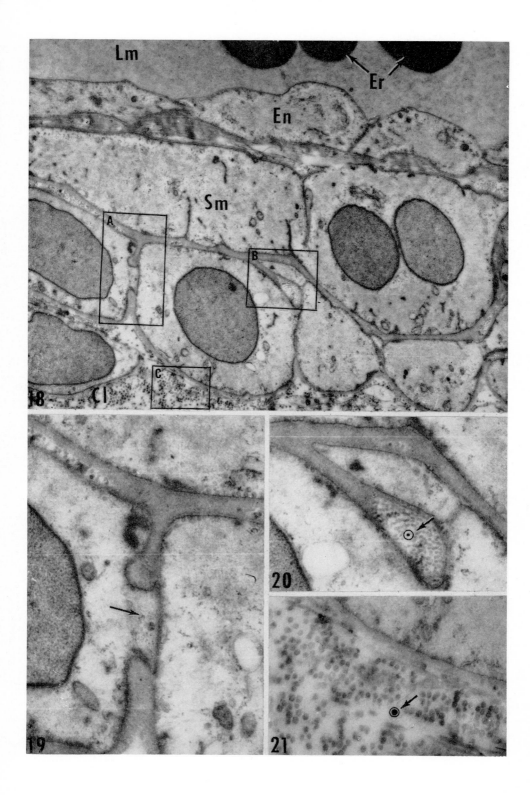

Lm

Er

En

Sm

A

B

C

Cl

18

19

20

21

Capillary Permeability and Transcapillary Exchange in Relation to Molecular Size

Eugene M. Renkin

George Washington University School of Medicine

The structure of the cells which make up the capillary endothelium is not visibly different from that of cells in general. We have the problem then of explaining the special properties of the capillary membrane with respect to the penetration of substances which do not penetrate the walls of most cells. Like cell membranes, capillary endothelium permits rapid passage of very low molecular weight substances and of substances soluble in lipids. But in addition to these, molecules of moderately large size which are insoluble in lipids penetrate readily, and even substances with molecular weights as high as those of the plasma proteins are transported in important quantities.

Table 1 lists measurements of capillary permeability to a series of lipid-insoluble materials over a wide range of molecular sizes, derived from the experimental data of Pappenheimer and his associates(1, 2). These values apply to capillaries in the skeletal muscles of the hind legs of cats. Two facts stand out. Substances of intermediate molecular weight like sucrose, raffinose, and inulin, which do not penetrate ordinary cell membranes, may pass across the capillary membrane not much less readily than the smallest molecules studied. And the permeability of the capillary wall to all these substances decreases regularly with increasing molecular size. Our problem is to determine what special features, anatomical or physiological, permit this membrane to exhibit these special permeabilities. At present, we are far from a complete solution.

One answer which has been suggested is that there are openings in the capillary wall, through or between the cells, through which the larger lipid-insoluble molecules may penetrate. If these openings or pores were approximately the size of molecules of serum albumin, we might be able to account on a geometrical basis for the rapid penetration of small molecules and the progressive restriction to permeation of larger molecules. This is, of course, only a hypothesis at present, since electron microscopists do not appear to be in agreement on whether or not suit-

---

The experimental work described hereafter was done in the Laboratory of Cardiovascular Physiology, National Heart Institute, Bethesda, Maryland.

able openings can be seen in their preparations of capillary walls. Its particular interest for the physiologist is that it permits him to construct a model of the capillary membrane and to compare its properties with those actually measured in living capillaries.

Imagine an inert membrane with a fibrous structure, and within this structure spacings between fibers of a size comparable to molecules of serum albumin. These openings are the pores. For mathematical simplicity, let us replace these irregular openings with uniform circular holes, keeping in mind that the dimensions of these represent only an idealized estimate of the spacings between fibers in our fibrous model. Our concept of a pore in this sense is thus only a name for a spacing of macromolecular size in the membrane.

The hypothetical capillary pores will be filled with the solvent which bathes both sides of the capillary wall, water. The diffusion of all substances within the pores and therefore their penetration through the membrane will depend at least in part on their free diffusibility in water. On this assumption, we can correct our estimates of capillary permeability for the progressive decrease in free diffusibility with increasing molecular size, and thus obtain a measure of the mechanical restriction to free diffusion of each molecule within the pores of the membrane. This is done by dividing each permeability coefficient in the third column of Table 1 by the free diffusion coefficient of each molecular species; the quotients are listed in the last column.

Although the tabulated figures indicate zero permeability to hemoglobin and serum albumin, it is amply evident that these molecules do penetrate the capillary walls in skeletal muscle. Their presence in lymph

TABLE 1. CAPILLARY PERMEABILITY TO A GRADED SERIES OF
LIPID-INSOLUBLE MOLECULES

Substance	Mol. Wt.	Permeability[a] Coefficient	P/D[b]
Water[c]	18	0.54×10^{-6}	17.2×10^{-3}
NaCl	58.5	.33	14.3
Urea	60	.26	13.5
Glucose	180	.090	10.0
Sucrose	342	.050	6.9
Raffinose	594	.039	6.0
Inulin	5100	.005	2.6
Myoglobin	17000	.0004	0.3
Hemoglobin	68000	.0000	0.0
Serum albumin	69000	.0000	0.0

[a] Mols/sec. diffusing per mol/L. concentration difference for each cm.^{2} capillary surface.

[b] Permeability coefficient divided by the free diffusion coefficient of each substance in water. Equivalent to effective pore area per unit path length per cm.^{2} capillary surface.

[c] The figures for water were obtained by extrapolation of the remaining data to the molecular weight of water.

from this source shows this clearly. However, their rates of penetration are very much less than those of the smaller molecules listed and are beyond the limits of sensitivity of the methods used. It would be more precise to say that capillary permeability to these large molecules corrected for differences in free diffusion rates is less than one per cent of that to water or urea.

From the figures in the last column of Table 1, which represent the degree of mechanical restriction offered by the hypothetical pores to penetration by a particular molecular species, it is possible to calculate the apparent mean size of the pores in the capillary wall. I shall not try to present here the mathematical analysis upon which these calculations are based; it has been published in full detail by Pappenheimer and his associates(1, 2). Restriction to penetration of an idealized spherical molecule through an idealized circular pore can be attributed to two kinds of interaction: (a) reflection at the pore entrance if the edge of the molecule strikes the edge of the pore, and (b) frictional resistance to motion within the pore once a molecule has entered. Factor (a) is easily calculated by means of elementary geometry. Factor (b) is more difficult to deal with, but fortunately is analogous to problems in hydraulic engineering which have been studied extensively and for which mathematical solutions are available. The final results of these calculations indicate that a pore radius of 30 Å (30 x 10^{-8} cm.) would closely reproduce the degree of restriction to molecular diffusion to lipid-insoluble substances shown by the capillary walls in mammalian skeletal muscle.

Application of the same methods to estimation of pore size in inert cellulose membranes has yielded values in close agreement with independent estimates (3). Allowing for uncertainties of theory and in measurement, we may assume the reliability of our estimate to be plus or minus 5 to 10 Å.

A second estimate of mean pore size in the capillary wall is based on measurements of fluid filtration under the influence of protein osmotic and hydrostatic forces according to Starling's Hypothesis. If filtered fluid moves through the hypothetical pores, it may be expected to follow the well-known laws of hydraulic flow in narrow channels, on the basis of which the radius of the pores may be calculated. Details of the calculations are contained in the references previously cited (1, 2). Mean pore radius thus measured was approximately 35 Å, in close agreement with the estimate based on restricted diffusion.

The size of a molecule just unable to penetrate the capillary wall may be taken as an estimate of the size of the largest pores present in any appreciable number. Taking hemoglobin (Table 1) as an estimate of "end-point" permeability, we arrive at a figure of 31 Å, which corresponds to physical estimates of the radius of this nearly spherical molecule. Most of the openings in the capillary membranes in mammalian skeletal muscle appear to lie close to 30 or 35 Å in radius (equivalent to a spacing of 60 to 70 Å between fibers in an irregular meshwork). The presence of a few openings of larger size may be indicated by the appearance of plasma albumins and globulins in lymph, but on the basis of measured permeabilities (Table 1), their contribution to the total pore area must be less than one per cent.

The hypothesis of pores in the capillary wall permits us to replace all the permeability data in Table 1 with only two numbers: (1) the mean pore radius, and (2) the permeability coefficient to water, which represents the total permeability of the pores with no restriction to diffusion. The simplification thus achieved and the high degree of internal consistency attained are not ends in themselves, but are valuable as a basis for further exploration, both physiological and anatomical, of the mechanisms by which materials are transported across the capillary endothelium.

In a few minutes, Dr. Sapirstein will speak about the problems involved in transport of large molecules across capillary membranes. I should like to devote the rest of my time to a discussion of the transport of the smaller molecules, those below the size of raffinose and sucrose. Included among the small molecules are many involved in the vital economy of the body, materials which must be supplied to the cells to be used in their metabolism and materials which must be carried away as wastes. Since appreciable amounts of such large molecules as the plasma proteins are transported across capillary walls into the lymph even though capillary permeability to these is immeasurable by techniques used to study permeability to small molecules, extremely high rates of transport are to be expected for the small molecules.

This is actually the case. If arteriovenous concentration differences are measured after adding to the blood various substances of low molecular weight, either in gross amounts or as isotopic tracers, large differences are observed. Thus in the course of a single passage through the capillary bed in mammalian skeletal muscle, 95 per cent of the D_2O or urea entering via the arterial blood may be lost, 65 per cent of the thiocyanate, and even 25 per cent of the inulin, and inulin is a rather large molecule by ordinary standards (4, 5).

If any substance is removed from the capillary blood to such an extent during the course of a single passage through a tissue, we can no longer consider capillary permeability and capillary surface area the only factors which limit transcapillary exchange. We shall have to consider also the supply of diffusible material in the blood entering the capillaries(6). Fig. 22 represents a simplified capillary of length H and surface area S. Arterial blood enters at rate Q ml./min., bearing a diffusible solute at concentration z_0. As the blood moves along the capillary, more and more

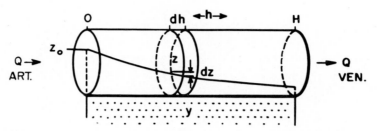

Fig. 22. Diagram of a capillary illustrating the derivation of the "Flow-Diffusion Equation." See the text for explanation.

of the solute escapes, and the internal concentration falls as shown in the diagram. In any small segment of the capillary (dh), diffusion takes place according to Fick's Law:

$$-M = PS(z - y), \tag{1}$$

where $-M$ is the quantity of solute lost per unit time by diffusion, P the capillary permeability coefficient to the solute, S the surface area of the segment, z the solute concentration within the segment, and y the solute concentration in the interstitial fluid outside. For such a segment, the law of conservation of matter demands that

$$loss = entry - exit.$$

Therefore

$$PS (z - y) = Qz - Q(z - dz), \tag{2}$$

where dz represents the fall of concentration within the segment. By integration of equation (2) over the length of the capillary, we may solve for the concentration of solute remaining in the venous blood (z_v). For simplicity, concentration of the solute in interstitial fluid is assumed to be zero.

$$z_v = z_o \, e^{-PS/Q}. \tag{3}$$

The symbol e represents the base of natural logarithms, 2.718 . . . and S is the total capillary surface area.

The fractional extraction (E) of solute from the capillary blood is equal to the arteriovenous difference divided by the arterial concentration:

$$E = \frac{z_o - z_v}{z_o} = 1 - e^{-PS/Q}. \tag{4}$$

This morning Dr. Zweifach suggested use of the concept "capillary clearance" as a convenient means of expressing the rates at which various substances are transported from capillaries to tissues. This term is clearly analogous to a renal clearance which represents the imaginary volume of blood from which a substance transported by the kidney is completely removed. In conformity with this usage, we may define the capillary clearance of any solute (C) as the product of total blood flow through a tissue and the fractional extraction of that solute from the blood. $C = QE$. Substitution in equation (4) leads to the following expression for capillary clearance in terms of blood flow, capillary permeability, and surface area:

$$C = Q\,(1 - e^{-PS/Q}). \tag{5}$$

The rate of transport of any solute from capillary blood to tissue is simply the product of capillary clearance and arterial concentration of that solute.

Equation (5), which has been called the "Flow-Diffusion Equation"(6) has the following properties of interest:

(1) Permeability and surface area appear only as a product. Changes in either cannot be surely distinguished without additional evidence. The permeability coefficient as used here includes not only the permeability of the capillary wall, but also that of any barriers to diffusion encountered outside the capillaries. It is an "over-all" permeability coefficient.

(2) At very low blood flows, capillary clearance becomes equal to blood flow, and transport is blood-flow limited.

(3) At very high flows, capillary clearance approaches the product PS as a limit. Transport is diffusion limited.

(4) At intermediate levels of blood flow, both flow and the permeability-surface area product affect capillary clearance. Theoretical curves describing clearance as a function of these variables are shown in Fig. 23.

To study the relation between flow and transport experimentally, capillary clearances of radioactive K^{42} were measured in isolated, artificially perfused skeletal muscles of dogs. Blood flow was varied over a wide range in each preparation by suitable adjustment of arterial perfusion pressure. Two Geiger counters recorded continuously the concentrations of K^{42} in arterial and venous blood. K^{42} extraction ratios and capillary clearances were calculated from the experimental data as follows:

$$K^{42}\ \text{extraction ratio} = \frac{\text{arterial counts/min.} - \text{venous counts/min.}}{\text{arterial counts/min.}}$$

$$K^{42}\ \text{capillary clearance} = K^{42}\ \text{extraction ratio} \times \text{blood flow.}$$

The choice of K^{42} as a tracer for these measurements is of particular importance. The quantity of potassium in the cells of a skeletal muscle is approximately 400 times as great as the plasma potassium in the vas-

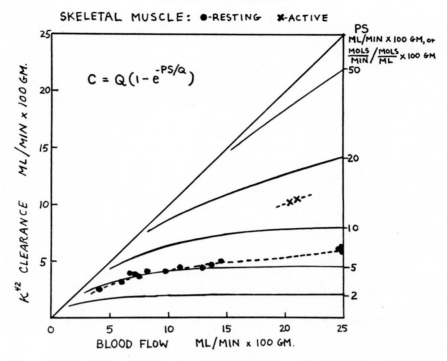

Fig. 23. Capillary K[42] clearances at various blood flow rates in an isolated skeletal muscle (dog's gracilis) at rest and during rhythmic activity. The smooth solid curves are drawn according to equation(5) for values of PS product shown in the right margin. The PS product of any experimental curve may be estimated by interpolation.

cular bed of the muscle. Due to the rapid exchange of potassium ions across muscle cell membranes, all particles of K[42] which leave the capillaries are almost immediately taken into the cells and mixed there with the large pool of non-radioactive intracellular potassium. Thus the accumulation of radioactivity outside the capillaries is minimal, and the simplifying assumption of zero outside concentration of the substance being transported can be used. The experimental results were consistent with this view.

When blood flow was varied by changing arterial perfusion pressure, K[42] extraction was found to be inversely related to the rate of blood flow over a range of flows considered to represent the physiological range for resting skeletal muscle (Table 2). Maximum extractions of about 90 per cent were seen in several experiments. As blood flow increased, K[42] extraction did not fall in strict inverse proportion, and capillary K[42] clearance increased steadily, as shown in the third column of the table. These changes were readily reversible and were reproducible in all preparations.

Consequently they confirm the theoretical prediction that blood flow is an important factor in determining rates of transcapillary exchange.

In Fig. 23, results of a series of K^{42} clearance measurements made on a single preparation are plotted on a background of theoretical flow-diffusion curves (equation 5). At first glance, the measured values conform rather closely to the theoretical curve for a permeability-surface area product equal to 5 mols/min. per mol/cm.^{3} concentration difference, except for a few values at unusually high rates of flow. Closer inspection of this and other records shows a small but distinct deviation from the theoretical curve for constant PS product. As blood flow—and arterial pressure—increases, PS appears to rise slightly. The change in this experiment was from 4 to 6 mols/min. per mol/cm.^{3} over a rather wide range.

A more considerable change in PS product is observed when blood flow is changed by some means other than varying the perfusion pressure. On the same graph are shown clearance measurements made during active vasodilatation produced by rhythmic contraction of the muscle under electrical stimulation. The PS product increased to three times its resting value. Local vasoconstriction induced by stimulation of sympathetic fibers innervating the muscle resulted in a fall in the PS product to half the control values, even when compared with controls at the same reduced rate of blood flow. The details of these experimental measurements will be published in the near future.

These few observations make it evident that there is an effect, and an important effect, of blood flow on the transport of materials from the capillary circulation. To a certain extent, transport of low molecular-weight substances is limited by blood flow as well as by permeability and by capillary surface area. It seems likely that the increased PS product observed during muscular exercise is due to a change in capillary surface rather than to a change in permeability per se, since the magnitude of the change agrees closely with reported histological estimates of the difference between the number of open capillaries in resting and exercising muscle(7). The same may be true of the fall in PS product with sympathetic stimulation. The most important physiological factors con-

TABLE 2. EFFECT OF BLOOD FLOW ON EXTRACTION RATIO AND CAPILLARY CLEARANCE OF K^{42} IN A BLOOD-PERFUSED DOG'S GRACILIS MUSCLE

Blood Flow ml./min. × 100 gm.	Extraction Fraction	K^{42} Clearance ml./min. × 100 gm.
1.9	0.78	1.5
4.0	0.67	2.7
8.6	0.50	4.3
12.9	0.43	5.6

Note: The weight of this muscle was 14 grams.

trolling transcapillary exchange may be concerned not with capillary permeability, but with the supply and distribution of blood in the capillary bed.

The flow-diffusion curves, theoretical and experimental, have important bearing on another problem of interest to microcirculatory physiologists, that of blood shunting in the minute vessels. The significance of Dr. Hyman's statement this morning about "physiological shunting" of blood may be illustrated on Fig. 23. If 15 ml. blood per minute flow through 100 grams of skeletal muscle, and only 5 ml. per minute are being "cleared" of K^{42}, the remaining 10 ml. blood flow per minute is effectively being shunted from artery to vein. It does not participate in the total exchange of potassium and might just as well have been diverted through anatomically distinct arteriovenous anastomoses. If we define physiological shunting as the flow of blood through a capillary bed in excess of the capillary clearance of important metabolic substrates, we may find this concept of value in dealing with the minute vessels and their functions.

REFERENCES

1. Pappenheimer, J. R., E. M. Renkin, and L. M. Borrero. Filtration, diffusion and molecular sieving through peripheral capillary membranes: A contribution to the pore theory of capillary permeability. Amer. J. Physiol. 167:13-46 (1951).
2. Pappenheimer, J. R. Passage of molecules through capillary walls. Physiol. Rev. 33:387-423 (1953).
3. Renkin, E. M. Filtration, diffusion, and molecular sieving through porous cellulose membranes. J. Gen. Physiol. 38:225-43 (1954).
4. Chinard, F. P., G. J. Vosburgh, and T. Enns. Transcapillary exchange of water and of other substances in certain organs of the dog. Amer. J. Physiol. 183:221-34 (1955).
5. Fries, E. D., T. F. Higgins, and H. J. Morowitz. Transcapillary exchange of deuterium oxide and thiocyanate in the forearm of man. J. Appl. Physiol. 5:526-32 (1952-53).
6. Renkin, E. M. Effects of blood flow on diffusion kinetics in isolated, perfused hind legs of cats: A double circulation hypothesis. Amer. J. Physiol. 183:125-36 (1955).
7. Martin, E. G., E. C. Woolley, and M. Miller. Capillary counts in resting and active muscles. Amer. J. Physiol. 100:407-16 (1932).

COMMENT

CHAIRMAN REYNOLDS: Thank you very much. Dr. Renkin has made it clear to us that we must think of dynamic factors in terms of exchange

Fig. 24. Longitudinally sectioned capillary of normal mouse cardiac muscle. L = capillary lumen; N = endothelial nucleus; m = mitochondria; er = endoplasmic reticulum. Numerous vesicles 50 mμ to 75 mμ in diameter appear throughout the cytoplasm; many open both into the lumen and into the peripheral space. (44,500 $\times$)

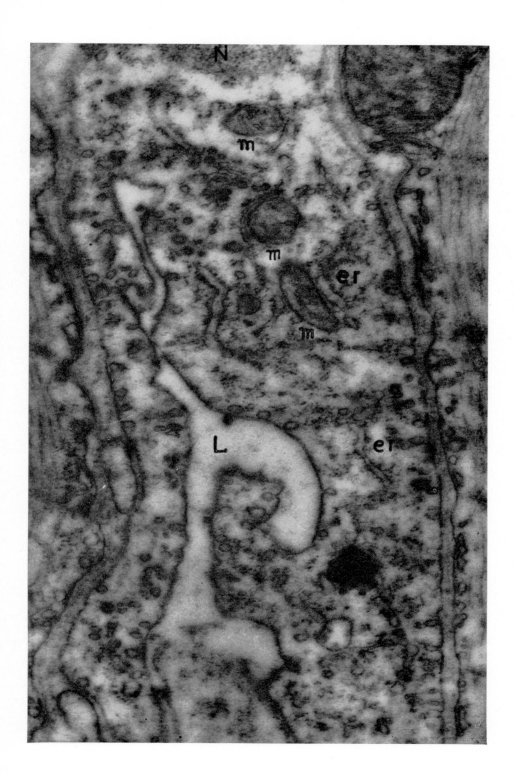

as well as morphological ones, and that there must be a common meeting ground between these somewhere.

[Recess]

CHAIRMAN REYNOLDS: I realize, from the two papers we have had so far, that we might have had discussion lasting for half a day, judging from the various comments that have been made to me and that I overheard in the hall. I think, however, that we will ask Dr. Dan Moore, formerly of Columbia University and now of the Rockefeller Institute for Medical Research, to make some remarks in relation to what has been said, and then, I believe, we will proceed, because of the lateness of the hour, to the next two papers. We will take time at the end for whatever discussion seems appropriate. I would like to call on Dr. Moore now.

DR. DAN H. MOORE: Thank you, Mr. Chairman. Dr. Fawcett has beautifully demonstrated the fine structure of capillaries and arterioles, and Dr. Renkin has illustrated the tremendous speed with which substances, particularly small molecules, can cross the barrier. I think that about all I can do is to add some more confusion to the problem.

This morning it was mentioned by Dr. Knisely that restriction in blood flow caused a decrease in capillary transfer, and this was again demonstrated this afternoon by Dr. Renkin in his graphs. I think that it might be interesting to consider for a moment what might happen to the structure of capillaries when the flow of blood is restricted.

We will review for a moment the complexity of capillary endothelium. This (Fig. 24) is a longitudinal section through a capillary between two muscle cells showing primarily the wall of a capillary. The lumen of the capillary being here, and it is possible to see, as Dr. Fawcett illustrated, these invaginations or indentations and the vesicles, and also the basement membrane, which in this case is quite narrow. The muscle cells are very close, and one sees exactly the same sort of invagination and formation of vesicles at the sarcolemma on the muscle side. Fig. 24 illustrates the extreme complexity of a normal muscle capillary.

Fig. 25 illustrates a capillary in its simplest form, a transverse section. Again one sees these vesicles which range in size from about 50 to 75 mμ. The frequency is not very great. There is a certain amount of space between these vesicles. Here is a joint, this being the simplest joint that is observed in the electron microscope. There is very little overlapping here.

Let us consider what may happen if we restrict the flow of blood. All the pictures I am showing are of mouse muscle, and we have simply

Fig. 25. Transverse section of normal mouse leg muscle capillary showing two endothelial joints and numerous small vesicles. (40,000 ×)

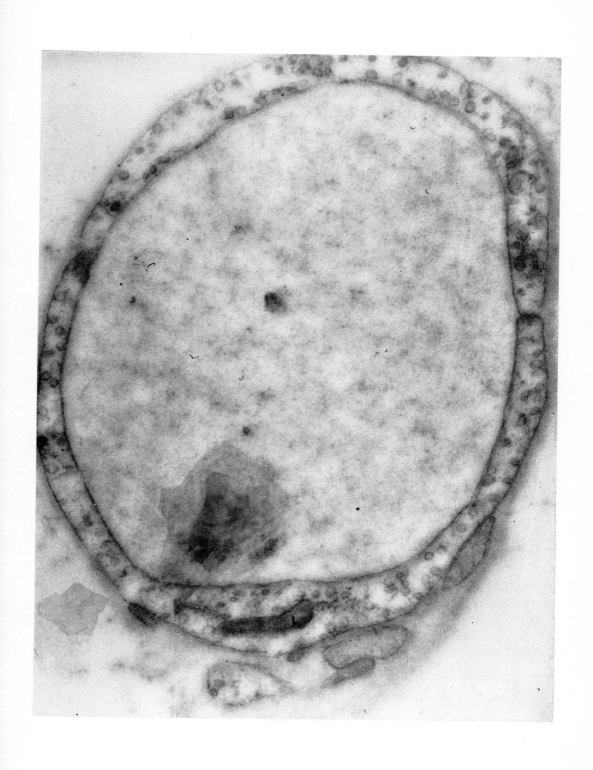

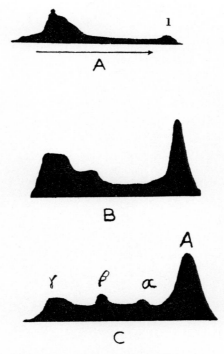

Fig. 26. Electrophoretic patterns of (A) normal mouse leg extract; (B) extract from legs 1 hour after release of two-hour tourniquets; (C) mixture of normal tissue extract (5 parts) and normal serum (1 part).

put a tight tourniquet on the mouse's leg. After a period of two hours, the muscle is severely damaged and, of course, there is a large amount of swelling. Material is passed from the lumen of the capillary to the extracellular space and possibly then into the muscle.

Fig. 26 compares saline extracts of normal and ischemic legs. These are electrophoretic patterns. This first one is a saline extract of normal mouse leg muscle; there is a trace of albumin, which, no doubt, has come from residual blood of the vascular bed. Then, after removal of a two-hour tourniquet, if you take an extract from the muscle, this is the kind of pattern one obtains. There is an enormous increase in the amount of albumin with practically no increase in globulin, as you can see.

If, however, one takes extract from normal legs and mixes it with serum, one obtains this kind of pattern, which has all the globulins pres-

Fig. 27. Capillary walls taken 10 minutes after the release of a two-hour tourniquet from a mouse's hind leg. The number and size of the vesicles are abnormally increased. (35,600 ×)

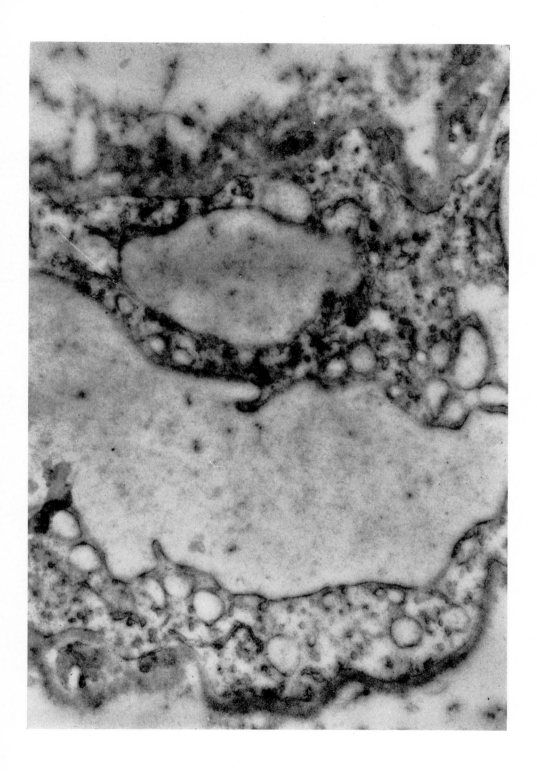

ent. The amount of albumin here is no larger than it is in the extract of injured limbs, but it is much broader, indicating an alpha$_1$ globulin (which is not separated very well here because it is in phosphate buffer of pH 7.4), and alpha$_2$ globulin, beta globulin, and gamma globulin; so it is quite clear that the breakdown of the barrier between the capillary and the muscle is not a complete breakdown.

In Fig. 27 we see what this injured capillary looks like. Instead of having the small vesicles, which were fewer in number, in some cases one finds this kind of a capillary. The vesicles may be very large. This one here is more than a micron in diameter. Many other vesicles are quite large, and they are certainly more numerous than they are in the normal capillary. The membranes on both sides of the endothelium are in most cases intact. There is no clear indication of a breakdown of the membrane. The basement membrane is also present in most places, particularly around here, but here it does not seem to be very evident. This is another thing that will also be evident in Figs. 28 and 29.

Fig. 28, again, shows a capillary after a two-hour tourniquet which had cut off most of the blood supply. You see the extremely dense basement membrane and the large number of vesicles. These are protrusions that extend up from behind or in front and are cross-sectioned in here with extremely large vesicles in the cell wall.

In Fig. 29, again we have this unusually dense basement membrane, and again the large number of large vesicles and the protrusions into the lumen of the capillary.

We will go back again just to refresh your memory of the normal. In a normal capillary the vesicles are almost all the same size. The walls are intact.

In a capillary from a muscle which had been made ischemic for only one hour (as compared with two hours), the damage is not nearly so severe. The vesicles are larger and more numerous, but there are none of the tremendous vesicles in the cell wall. There may be considerable damage in the muscle with mitochondrial damage. At two and a quarter hours, with the tourniquet removed for six minutes, one sees very large vesicles, and the cell membrane seems to be intact. In this case, there is very little basement membrane.

The meaning of all this, of course, is not very obvious. We don't know what is going on. There is swelling. The total weight of this limb is about doubled. There is swelling in the tissue and there is swelling in the capillary wall, but, at least, these vesicles are increased in size.

Fig. 28. Capillary of mouse leg muscle 10 minutes after release of a two-hour tourniquet. The very dense basement membrane may indicate the proximity of the arteriole. The size and frequency of the vesicles are markedly increased. (35,600 ×)

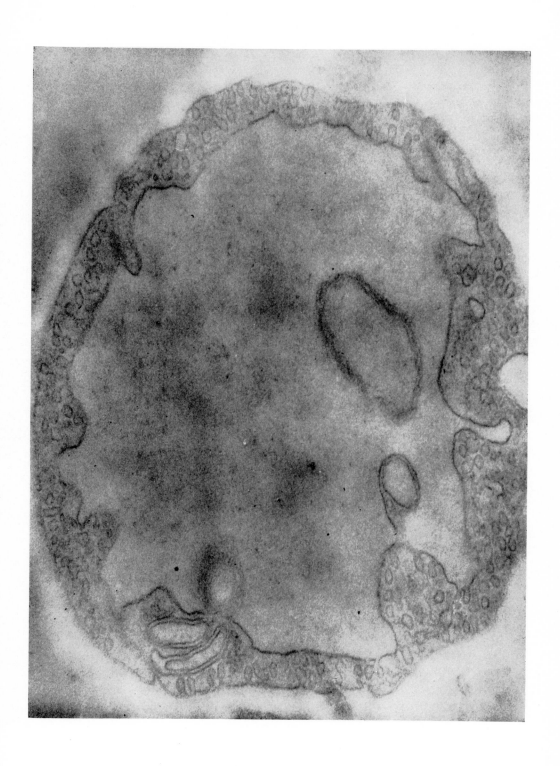

Another point that might be made about protein transfer across capillary walls—and I am sure that you are familiar with this—is in the placenta. Fig. 30 shows electrophoretic patterns of human fetal and maternal blood. The gamma globulin that is in the fetus (cord blood) has come entirely from the mother. It has been shown by tissue culture that the albumin can be synthesized in the fetal liver, but there is no evidence that gamma globulin can be synthesized in the fetus at all, and the newborn child is immune to the same things that the mother is immune to; there is a great deal of evidence that this gamma globulin, which has a molecular weight of twice that of albumin, is transferred across the placental membrane, and the capillaries in the placenta have the same vesicular structure as the capillaries I have shown you. Here we have a higher gamma globulin in the fetal blood than in the maternal blood, so there has been a selective transfer of gamma globulin across the membrane.

A photograph shows what was obtained in the experiments which Dr. Fawcett mentioned earlier this afternoon—the experiments of Dr. S. L. Wissig(22) and Dr. G. E. Palade (unpublished data) at the Rockefeller Institute, who visualized ferritin injected into rats. The specimen shown was taken ten minutes after about 3 to 4 ml. of concentrated ferritin solution was injected into an artery. One sees the particles of ferritin. These are of a little under 100 Å in diameter. The lumen of the capillary is clear; the ferritin particles show, as well as one of the vesicles, which shows in its lumen some of the ferritin particles. Some ferritin particles seem to be free in the cytoplasm of the endothelial cell but may be connected with vesicles. There are ferritin particles in the basement membrane and in many other places, as is illustrated in the micrographs of their exhibit at the Anatomy Meetings. They are found outside, they are found in the cytoplasm, they are found in the vesicles, and, very rarely, they are found in the endothelial joints. However, there are instances where one finds the particles in the joints.

The only summary, I think, that can be made from this whole discussion is that we simply do not know how materials are transferred across capillary walls. It is likely that there is more than one route of transfer. Certainly, from these experiments and particularly the ferritin experiments, it is possible for materials to be caught in these vesicles and transferred across. It is also possible that there may be transfer through the joints between the endothelial cells. The vesicles may carry them all the way across intact, or the vesicles may liberate them in the cytoplasm of

Fig. 29. Mouse leg muscle capillary taken one hour after application of tourniquet which was not released. The frequency of vesicles is greater than normal and the size is somewhat increased. Epoxy embedding. (56,000 ×)

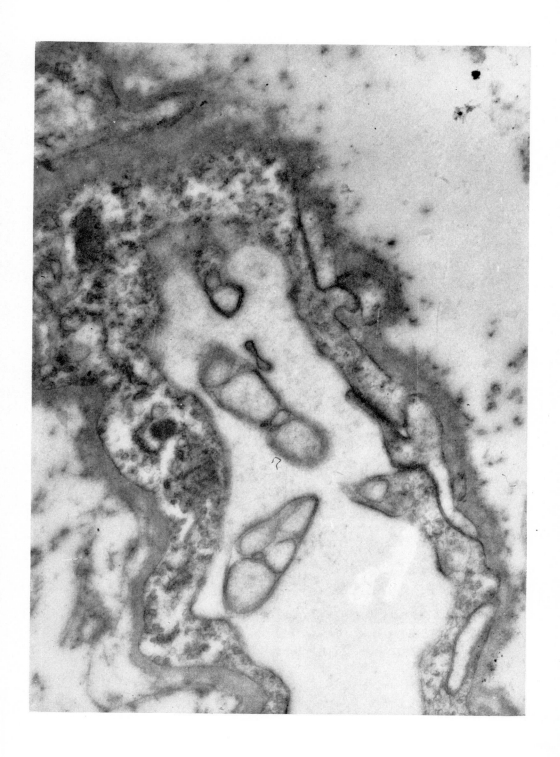

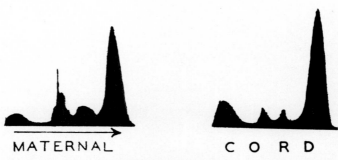

MATERNAL   C O R D

Fig. 30. Electrophoretic patterns of maternal and newborn infant sera showing the elevated γ-globulin in the infant serum. This γ-globulin is apparently preferentially transferred through the placental capillaries.

the endothelium and pick them up again. It just is not known how this transfer takes place, entirely.

CHAIRMAN REYNOLDS: Thank you, Dr. Moore. Once again, we are brought back to the vesicle problem, aren't we? I would like to call now on Dr. Leo Sapirstein, of the Department of Physiology of the Ohio State University School of Medicine, who is going to talk on "Macromolecular Exchanges in Capillaries." Maybe he will have an answer about these vesicles.

Macromolecular Exchanges in Capillaries

Leo Sapirstein

Department of Physiology, Ohio State University School of Medicine

Mr. Chairman, Ladies and Gentlemen: I regret to say that I have no answer to the question of the vesicles. The subject of this talk is the passage of macromolecules across capillary walls, and perhaps it should be subtitled, "The Capillary Wall is Not a Barrier to Anything."

Whereas the essayists so far have caused considerable cerebration, at least I can vouch for myself, all I propose to do is to cause great pain, because I intend to question some fairly basic notions. Because of the fact that I am questioning basic notions let me start by raising a question with an apparently obvious answer: Why is it generally believed that the capillary wall does confine proteins? The basis for this belief rests on the virtual equivalence, which was postulated by Starling[1], and later demonstrated by Landis[2] and Pappenheimer and Soto-Rivera[3], between the colloidal osmotic pressure of the plasma proteins and the hydrostatic pressure within the capillary. The fact of this equivalence suggests that there must exist a surface against which it is asserted, and it seems perfectly reasonable to assume that this surface is one which is microscopically visible, namely, the capillary wall.

Let me restate this proposition in the first slide (see Diagram 1). This

DIAGRAM 1. EQUIVALENCE OF COLLOID OSMOTIC PRESSURE AND HYDROSTATIC PRESSURE ACROSS THE WALLS OF THE MINUTE VESSELS

COP_T	HP_T	
COP_P	HP_P	MEMBRANOUS BARRIER PRESUMED TO BE THE CAPILLARY WALL
COP_T	HP_T	

$$HP_P - COP_P = HP_T - COP_T$$

Note: HP_P = hydrostatic pressure of blood
COP_P = osmotic pressure of plasma proteins
HP_T = hydrostatic pressure tissue space
COP_T = osmotic pressure of proteins in tissue space

47

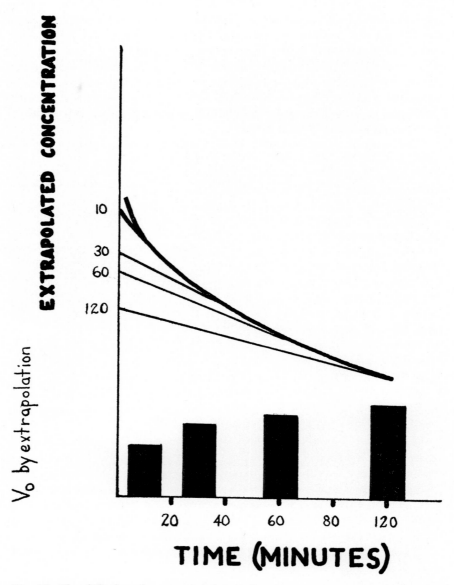

Fig. 31. The difficulty of appropriate extrapolation of a disappearance curve of a plasma protein label is illustrated. The continuous curve shows a typical disappearance curve. Extrapolation of this curve to zero time can be made to yield variable answers depending on the portion of the curve used for making the extrapolation. The calculated volume of distribution of the label varies accordingly.

is the basic proposition upon which we base our belief that the capillary endothelium is not permeable to proteins. The colloidal osmotic pressure of the plasma proteins is approximately equivalent to the hydrostatic pressure which exists in the plasma. You will note that I have indicated here that the barrier, across which this difference is asserted, is presumed to be the capillary wall. It is presumed to be so, and one can see the capillary wall, but there is no actual evidence at this moment that the barrier is the capillary wall, and, in fact, I propose to present evidence now which indicates that it is not.

The basic observation which focuses attention on the possibility that the barrier is not the capillary wall is the fact that when one estimates the plasma volume by the use of substances which label the plasma proteins, invariably—and this has occurred with almost everyone who has done the experiment—the plasma volume so obtained exceeds the plasma volume calculated from the distribution volume of the red cells and the hematocrit of the large vessel blood.

Four explanations for this discrepancy come to mind. The first is that there has been an error in the estimation of the plasma volume by the use of dye of such nature that the distribution volume is overestimated. The second possibility is that there is in small vessels a layer of plasma which is available for mixing with plasma labels but which is not available for penetration by labelled cells.

The third possibility is that certain organs possess extra plasma while other organs do not, so that when we speak of the extra plasma of the body we are, in fact, referring to extra plasma in particular organs only.

The fourth possibility, which appears to have been systematically overlooked, is the possibility that there is, in fact, extra plasma outside the capillary blood vessels throughout the body.

Let us start with the first proposition. This is the proposition that we have made a mistake in estimating the plasma volume by the use of dye. In the estimation of plasma volume by the use of dyes which label proteins, or by the use of radioactive labelled plasma proteins, invariably one obtains a declining concentration curve. You will remember that in order to calculate distribution volume, we must divide the amount of label injected by the concentration of label. Now, clearly, if we have a declining concentration curve of label, we can make no calculation whatsoever.

Well, the easy solution to this is, of course, to make a reasonable extrapolation of the concentration curve to zero time. Clearly the label is being lost from the circulation. Clearly we cannot take the actual concentration at zero time, because then mixing is not yet complete. Therefore, we must extrapolate the curve back to zero time so that we can define the

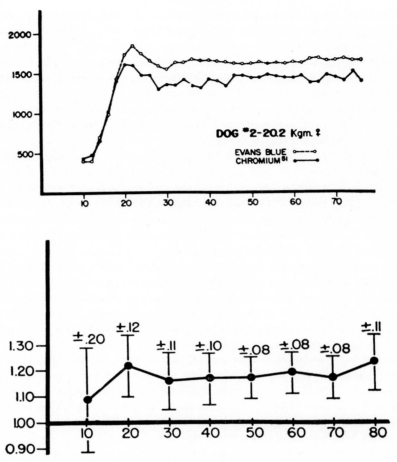

Fig. 32a. Apparent distribution volumes of Cr^{51} and T-1824 (*ordinate*, milliliters) as a function of time in seconds following injection (*abscissa*).

Fig. 32b. Results. Ratio Evans blue dye/Cr^{51} volumes (*ordinate*) with time (*abscissa*, in seconds). Standard deviations indicated.

concentration as it would have been in the presence of mixing, but in the absence of loss of label.

Unfortunately for this kind of approach, the declining curve of plasma protein labels follows no simple pattern. Consequently, any extrapolation made to zero time is at best an extrapolation by eye. As is shown in Fig. 31, which describes the results of a typical experiment with a plasma protein label, the extrapolated value at zero time is entirely dependent upon the data chosen for making the extrapolation. For example, if the extrapolation were made on the basis of data observed between 60 and 120 minutes, the zero intercept would be much lower than that obtained by extrapolating the data observed between 10 and 30 minutes. The distribution volume would be correspondingly less if the earlier data were employed.

Now, is it possible that, just as we were able to make the plasma volume appear to shrink by extrapolating from earlier data, we may be able to shrink the plasma volume enough to take care of our discrepancy by making our observations at an early enough time and making the right kind of extrapolation? Unfortunately, we don't know what the right kind of extrapolation is, for the disappearance curves follow no simple law.

The need for extrapolation can be avoided simply by making observations very early in time and using the observations as such rather than as the basis for a construction.

Fig. 32 shows the results of experiments(4) in which this was done. On top we see the apparent volume of distribution of Evans blue-labelled plasma proteins and chromium-labelled red cells in a dog, observed at intervals of seconds after their simultaneous injection. As you see, there is no need for extrapolation here. But observe this: the top curve describes the volume of distribution of Evans. The bottom curve describes the volume of distribution of labelled chromium. The difference is fully materialized within 20 seconds. There is no extrapolation here. We have not made a mistake in the estimation of plasma volume at all. The explanation is fallacious.

The lower graph describes the results in a set of nine dogs. In each of these dogs, the apparent volume of the plasma by the dye method is referred to the plasma volume by the chromium method—this is the labelled red-cell method—the latter being considered as 1. Observe that at 10 seconds, the difference has already been established in part. At 20 seconds it is fully manifest, and it continues throughout the period of observation. These findings indicated that the source of the discrepancy is not to be sought in faulty estimation of the plasma volume by extrapolation. We are left with the second, third, and fourth alternatives to account for the extra plasma of the organism.

Well, let's go on to the second alternative. The second alternative is by all means today the most popular, and I am afraid that I can't quite get out of this explanation; not quite, but almost.

We have excess plasma in the organism. In a way, this is very easy to account for, if we say the following: that when blood enters a small blood vessel, or, in fact, when blood moves into any blood vessel, it deposits, so to speak, a layer of what was called in the 1920's, by Smith, Arnold, and Whipple(5), "still" plasma, at the border. This "still" plasma, as its name implies, seems to sit still.

Within this lining of "still" plasma there flows whole blood. The corpuscles of this blood do not invade the "still" plasma and so if we administer a corpuscle label, we will measure not the total volume enclosed

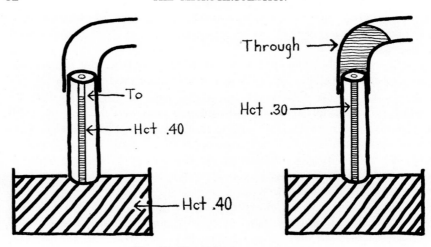

Fig. 33. The Fahraeus experiment.

by endothelium, but a smaller volume—that which is bounded by the layer of "still" plasma. If, on the other hand, we administer a plasma label, we will measure the whole volume, for the "still" plasma is available for mixing with dissolved materials.

This point of view gains considerable support from the classical experiments of Fahraeus(6) which are shown in Fig. 33. I think, if any of you are not familiar with this experiment, it may at first sight be baffling. It was to me, for a long time. Fahraeus drew blood with a hematocrit of, say, 0.40 into a capillary tube, up to the end. He measured the hematocrit of the blood now contained in this tube, and, as one might suspect, the hematocrit of this blood was, indeed, 0.40. If, on the other hand, he used the same capillary tube and the same blood, but pulled the blood to the end of the tube and then through it, the hematocrit of the blood which stayed behind in the tube was only 0.30. This type of effect was observed in tubing of diameter of 0.10 mm. or less.

This phenomenon is explicable in this way. When blood is taken to the end of the capillary tube, it must be representative blood. It cannot have undergone any changes in composition except from top to bottom. On the other hand, when blood has passed through the tube, it has left behind a layer of "still" plasma. The corpuscles, according to Fahraeus, are being accelerated in this tube. They go through faster. The plasma is slow. The slow plasma contaminates the blood which remains in the tube.

It is a beautiful experiment. I tried for about six months to repeat it and I couldn't. It is a very hard experiment to do, technically; despite the fact that I couldn't repeat it, I believe it, for reasons which will be shown in Fig. 34, top.

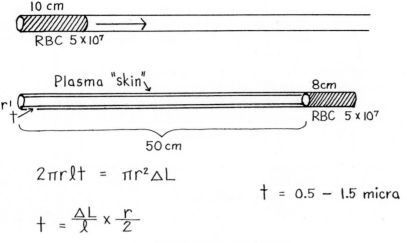

$$2\pi r \ell t = \pi r^2 \Delta L$$

$$t = 0.5 - 1.5 \text{ micra}$$

$$t = \frac{\Delta L}{\ell} \times \frac{r}{2}$$

Fig. 34. Modified Fahraeus experiment.

The experiment can be modified in such a way that it becomes technically feasible and preserves the gist of the original. This is done as follows. Either polyethylene or glass tubing is used. A column of blood of an appropriate length is drawn into a capillary tube, and by gentle suction is advanced through the length of the tube. As this train of blood moves, it can be seen to shrink. Oddly enough, however, the train of blood when it has passed through the entire length of the tube has lost no corpuscles. This can be established by making a red-cell count or a hemoglobin determination. The shrinking of the train is due entirely to the loss of plasma at the surface in the tube. This is the "still" plasma of which Smith, Arnold, and Whipple spoke; this is the slow plasma of Fahraeus.

Now, from a knowledge of the distance through which the column of blood has traveled, from a knowledge of the shrinking, and from simple geometric considerations, one can immediately calculate the thickness of the layer of plasma which coats the inside of the tube. The thickness of this layer is entirely independent of the composition of the tube, it seems to be independent of the rate at which the blood is pulled, and it is independent of temperature.

The procedure and the equations which are used for the calculations of the thickness of the thin layer are shown in Fig. 34, bottom. In repeated experiments on human blood, we have found that the thickness of this layer of "still" plasma is between 0.5 and 1.5 μ.[1]

[1] Since the presentation of this speech, there has appeared a report of a similar experiment by Copley(7). Copley's experiments indicated that the layer is occasionally thicker than the value given here. The reason for the discrepancy is not known.

Let us return to the original question of the location of excess plasma in the organism. Will this layer of "still" plasma, which is not a part of the distribution volume of labelled corpuscles but is a part of the distribution part of plasma label, account for it?

I am inclined to think not. On the other hand, the arguments on which this conclusion is based require that two major assumptions be made. I am not certain these assumptions are valid, and I do not think that we can come to a final answer at this time regarding the validity of this as an explanation of the extra plasma.

The assumptions which I made were these: first, that 15 per cent of the volume of blood in the body is contained in tubing of such size that this effect is maximized. This means 20-micron diameter tubes, because in tubes which are less than 20 micra in diameter this effect no longer occurs; second, that the layer of "still" plasma is just as thick in blood vessels as it is in glass or polyethylene.

Calculating that the 15 per cent of the blood volume is in tubing of exactly 20 micra in diameter, the most favorable assumption which can be made, the volume of excess plasma which one could expect to find in a 70-kilo man is of the order of 100 cc. However, the 70-kilo man would have a difference between the plasma volume by dye and the plasma volume by the red-cell method of somewhere around 500 cc. The discrepancy seems too large for the proposed explanation to be correct.

Well, let's turn to the third explanation. The third explanation is simple. It says: Of course, there is excess plasma in the organism, but this excess plasma is confined to a few organs. Everybody knows that the liver capillaries are permeable to proteins. Furthermore, evidence has been presented recently that the kidney may be included in the group of organs which contain excess plasma. Pappenheimer and Kinter(8) have summarized the evidence which bears on this point and have proposed an explanation for its presence based on the vascular architecture of the kidney.

To investigate the possibility that this was the explanation, studies were carried out on the excess plasma content of various organs of the rat(9). The plasma was labelled with iodinated albumin and the cells were labelled with chromium. By making simultaneous labels in the same animals, a good deal of variability was eliminated. Determinations were then made of the amount of plasma and red cells in each organ. To make the numbers easier to understand, I have expressed the ratio of cell volume to cell plus plasma volume (organ hematocrit) in terms of the large vessel hematocrit.

Table 3 shows the results of these experiments. At first sight, it appears that we have found the answer and that excess plasma is, indeed, located in the liver and perhaps the kidney. These organs have hematocrits which are much lower than that of the large vessel blood.

TABLE 3. RAT ORGAN HEMATOCRIT/LARGE VESSELS HEMATOCRIT

	Time (seconds)				Number of Animals
	30	60	120	300	
Liver	.48	.53	.46	.55	20
Kidney	.57	.59	.44	.44	20
Gut	.63	.59	.62	.53	20
Heart	.64	.77	.66	.68	20
Lungs	.68	.64	.57	.66	20
Brain	.90	.72	.85	.75	20
Carcass	.70	.72	.63	.60	8
Spleen	1.00	1.09	1.28	1.52	20
Large Vessels	1.00	1.00	1.00	1.00	

But the gut must also be included and so also must the heart and the lungs. We must even add the brain, which also can be seen to have excess plasma. The skin has excess plasma just like all the other organs and so also does the carcass. We must conclude, therefore, that excess plasma is not located in any particular organ, but that wherever a vascular bed exists there is excess plasma.

Those of us who are familiar with detective novels will be aware of the fact that when all possible explanations of a crime have been exhausted, then the remaining explanation must be correct even if it is improbable. In this case, we have exhausted the three most likely explanations for the presence of excess plasma, and we must, therefore, turn to our remaining possibility, unpleasant as it may seem. Fig. 35 presents this last "improbable" alternative. It indicates that plasma is both inside and outside the capillary endothelium, but we must add one item. The volume of excess plasma is not so great that it occupies the entire interstitial space. It is barred from some of it. Let us, then, insert a barrier as is shown in Fig. 35.

This is the fourth and final solution that occurs, at least to me. The reason why we have excess plasma is because there *is* excess plasma around the capillary. The reason it does not go throughout the interstitial space is because there is a barrier. It would be nice if there were an anatomical demonstration of this.

There is. Fig. 36 illustrates an experiment which was done in 1926 by Heimberger(10). This is not Heimberger's picture, because he did not include a picture. The description of all this is in the fine print. I asked the artist to draw this from the translated text. This diagram, just like the one before, says that we have an interstitial space which is not homogeneous. There is a liquid in here adjacent to the capillary (the pericapillary lymph), and outside this there is a solid.

Here is Heimberger's statement: "If intradermal gas is produced by electrolysis, with a fine needle introduced through the skin, the picture usually observed is the formation of a large gas bubble which pushes

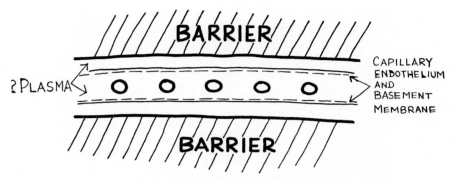

Fig. 35. Potential extravascular portion of barrier.

aside the surrounding tissue." This is exactly what one would expect from electrolysis, producing gas in the midst of a solid. "But," he says, "a completely different picture is seen if the needle is brought closer to the capillary wall. Suddenly, we see an enormous number of very small bubbles which form a kind of a veil all around the capillary and along the capillary, almost throughout its length." The next part is not indicated in the picture. "From this veil, branches sometimes go to other capillaries or end blindly somewhere within the tissue. The shape of the capillary is surprisingly little changed by these bubbles, and very soon it can be seen again through the disappearing bubbles in almost its original form."

This conclusion is also worth stating. I don't have the literal translation, but Heimberger states that these observations suggest the existence of a pericapillary lymph space all along and all around the capillary.

Well, there we have our diagram. One trouble exists. You remember how we began. I said that the reason why we believe that proteins are confined within capillary walls is the fact that colloid osmotic pressure and hydrostatic pressure are demonstrably equivalent or nearly equivalent to each other. Here we have a barrier, but where is the interface against which the equality of the protein osmotic pressure and the capillary hydrostatic pressure are made manifest?

That is not so hard to find. We can simply invent it (Fig. 37). Let us include a lymphatic in the diagram. We have clear fluid within the lymphatic capillary and clear fluid in and around the capillary. The capillary endothelium is represented as confining nothing whatsoever, except only red cells. Outside the endothelium, we have pericapillary lymph, which is really plasma. This is our extra plasma. Between the pericapillary lymph and the true lymphatic is the membrane across which Starling's hypothesis is made manifest. Across this solid, the colloid osmotic pressure and hydrostatic pressure can be equal to each other.

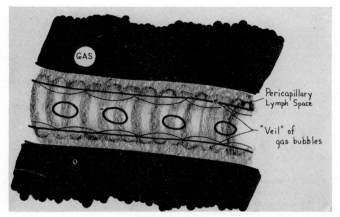

Fig. 36. Pericapillary electrolysis. Drawn from Heimberger's description.

The liquids which are separated from each other are true lymph and pericapillary lymph, and the membrane is ground substance, whatever that is. I hate to use the name, because I can't seem to find anybody who seems to be willing to say exactly what it is.

I would suggest that the membrane across which exchanges of material occur between the blood and the cells has been misidentified. The classic view has it that exchanges occur across the capillary endothelium. I am suggesting the possibility that the barrier across which exchanges occur is separated by some distance from the capillary wall. The ground substance, if this concept is correct, is where exchanges are moderated. This is the barrier which we have to consider in considering the movement of materials between the capillary and the lymph, on the one hand, and between the capillary and the tissue space, on the other.

I want to say one more word. Most studies which have been made of the capillary wall are practically consistent with this hypothesis, because most workers who have studied the capillary wall, particularly in terms of the equivalence of hydrostatic and osmotic pressure, have not looked at the capillary wall at all except later in making their calculations. Likewise, most persons who have determined transfer of materials across capillary walls by the disappearance curves of materials from the blood have not looked at the capillary wall.

In all these experiments, it is as easy to understand the results, as consistent with the conclusions, to substitute for the words, "capillary wall" the words, "hematolymph barrier," which I would for the moment identify as the ground substance.

I would like to summarize these thoughts by suggesting that the anatomical capillary wall may not act as a barrier to macromolecules; at the same time there may exist a barrier external to this anatomical capillary

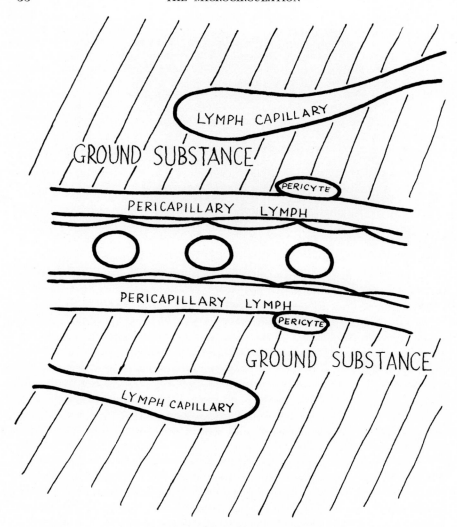

Fig. 37. Hematolymph barrier.

wall which has the physical properties ordinarily attributed to the capillary wall and which is relatively impermeable to macromolecules.

REFERENCES

1. Starling, E. H. On the absorption of fluids from the connective tissue spaces. J. Physiol. *19*:312-26 (1896).
2. Landis, E. M. Micro-injection studies of capillary permeability. II. The relation between capillary pressure and walls of single capillaries. Amer. J. Physiol. *82*:217-38 (1927).

the use of *non*-isometric models. Their conclusions about model testing should be of real interest to us. It would appear that model tests are valid only under certain very special circumstances. May I review them briefly?

Sometimes, changes in the dimensionless constants of an equation, such as Reynolds number, Webers number, Froude number, etc., may make a model study possible or realistic. In other cases, a dilatation of the form of the model, so that one dimension of the model is distorted with respect to the other dimension, will make the model perform in a manner comparable to the prototype. In every case, however, experienced investigators, dealing with model studies, refuse to use the data derived on a model without a test on the full-sized prototype. I propose that every physical phenomenon dealing with microstructures, whether they be biological or otherwise, must be tested with an appropriate isometric model.

For these reasons, we have attempted in a systematic fashion to make isometric replicas of the basement membrane, with particular attention to the pores or fixed interspaces. It very early became apparent that a number of physical forces conspire to make certain microstructures possible and stable. It will be my purpose to discuss the techniques of micro-replication that bear on the membrane problem as well as to discuss some of the physical forces which play a role in stabilizing certain elements of the membrane.

To begin with, let us take the simplest kind of barrier. This is probably the kind of barrier that exists between oil and water, or water and air, a so-called interface. This does not imply that such barriers in their gross form are anything like the membranes we wish to prepare, but a preliminary study of interfaces gives some information bearing on our problem of isometric replication.

In order to adapt an interface for use in a membrane, a device for stabilizing this interface is apparently necessary. It has often been postulated that an interface between two bulk phases is an integral part of the structure of membrane. Such an interface in a membrane would, in most situations, have a small cross-sectional area. The interface might even be the essential part of a pore. A clue as to how the interface between bulk phases is stabilized has been found in a phenomenon observed with the air-water interface. This phenomenon will be referred to here as an aperture effect. In part, it is related to an observation made by Cassie and Baxter in 1944(1). May I review this experiment?

Cassie and Baxter carried out, actually, a very simple experiment. What they were interested in was the effect of porosity of a solid surface on the contact angle of the surface with water. To investigate this, they constructed four grids of parallel wires. They used two different wire diameters, each set being spaced at different intervals apart in the grid.

WETTABILITY OF SOLID SURFACE

r = RADIUS OF FIBER d = ½ SPACE BETWEEN FIBERS

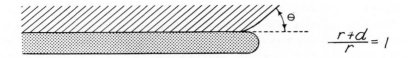

$$\frac{r+d}{r} = 1$$

WETTABILITY OF GRIDS

r = RADIUS OF FIBER d = ½ SPACE BETWEEN FIBERS

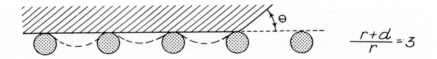

$$\frac{r+d}{r} = 2$$

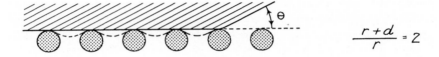

$$\frac{r+d}{r} = 3$$

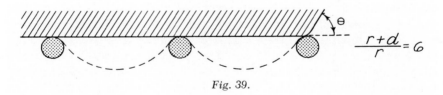

$$\frac{r+d}{r} = 6$$

Fig. 39.

In Fig. 39 I have given certain relationships which have developed between the grid, the wire diameter, and the spacing between the wires. Here the grids are shown in cross-section. The wires are circles. The imaginary plane of the surface, established by a series of parallel wires set at equal intervals along the plane, is drawn by this heavy dark line. If one suspends a drop of water on the surface of the grid, one will find that the water drops down like a slack clothesline between the wires. If the wires are coated with paraffin and are large, one can, surprisingly enough, demonstrate that the contact angle with this imaginary surface, going from close spacing to distant spacing, gradually increases.

If the contact angle is a measure of the wettability of the imaginary interface, the form, with the greatest ratio between the space and the wire diameter shows the maximum of *non*-wettability. This is not what one expects.

In fact, if a drop of water is suspended on a grid of coarse fibers, 4 μ in diameter, spaced 12 μ apart, one finds that this is held tenaciously on the coarse fibers (Fig. 40). The fibers themselves are wetted, the same as clean glass.

What Cassie and Baxter showed, really, was that if you called the wire diameter r, and half the distance between the wires d, a relationship exists between these two values and the wettability of the grid. The wettability increases as a function of $\frac{r + d}{r}$. This phenomenon of non-wettability of the imaginary surface, most of which is composed of empty space between wires, has the additional and related effect of stabilizing an interface between air and water. This stabilizing effect I want to call the aperture effect.

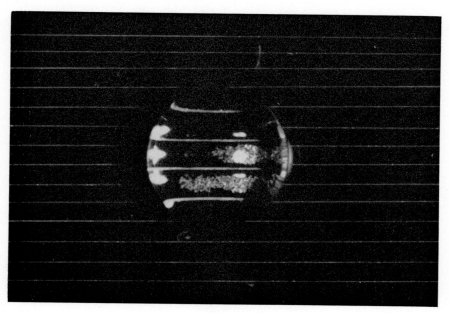

Fig. 40.

It should be apparent—and I shall develop this concept as it relates to membranes and, in particular, as it relates to the general problem of size and of isometric replication—that the phenomenon of non-wettability of a grid of wires at its imaginary surface is not quite the same as the aperture effect.

The aperture effect depends, in addition, on the relative size of the aperture, and it should be intuitively apparent to you that, if the ratio is kept constant, the interface between the wires will be much more stable when they are close together than when they are far apart.

We first observed this aperture effect when studying quartz fiber grids of very much smaller diameter than the wire grids of Cassie and

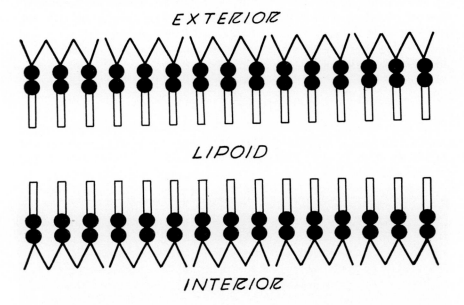

Fig. 41.

Baxter. In the case of Cassie and Baxter wires of 70 to 130 μ in diameter were used.

The nonpenetrance of water into the small space between these wires seems superficially at variance with the laws of capillarity. On superficial analysis it would appear that water should enter this space readily and eagerly, rather than to resist such entry. However, this is an aperture effect and actually depends on the diameter and, consequently, the radius of curvature of the portal of entry for water into the supposed capillary. You will readily see that there is a vital difference between the capillary and the aperture effect.

Probably the only instance in which a stabilized air-water interface in a membrane is of interest to us as biologists is that of the lung and external coverings of the body, whatever they may be anatomically. It would be of more general interest to know if this aperture effect can be used to stabilize a water-water interface and hence act as part of the membrane complex in other situations.

I should like to review two experiments, carried out twenty years ago, which have a bearing on the problem of stabilizing a water-water interface.

The first experiment was carried out by Danielli. It was very simple and very ingenious. Danielli postulated, as Fig. 41 indicates, that the arrangement of molecules of the cell wall is such that the center of the membrane is composed of a lipoid layer oriented with the polar group facing inside and outside, and that they are covered inside and outside with a monolayer of proteins.

What Danielli really needed to do was to demonstrate how this could be accomplished in fact as well as in theory(2).

To do this, Danielli took a drop of saline (Fig. 42), which was heavier than a lipid solution, and a salt solution, and dropped it through both solutions. The protein molecules are oriented on the outside of the water

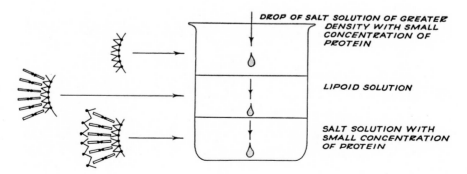

Fig. 42.

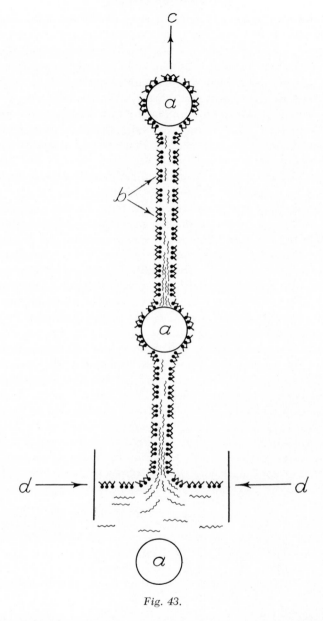

Fig. 43.

drop. As it passed through the lipid solution, it collected a properly organized lipid bimolecular layer and, as it entered the last phase, a protein solution, it gathered the final part of this complex, protein-lipid-
protein.

This arrangement was stable under the conditions of the experiment, but, unfortunately, did not lend itself to further studies on membrane permeability.

Shortly after this, however, Langmuir(3), taking a protein layer, suspended at an oil-water interface, found that he could lift this protein layer off with a wire loop of about 8 mm. in diameter. Langmuir was able to keep some of these films intact in air. These were apparently bimolecular layers of protein. They were stretched across an 8 mm. span. Unfortunately, when Langmuir resuspended these in water, he found that the protein dissolved off frequently, and that they were unsatisfactory for studying the transport across such organized complexes of lipid or protein.

In reviewing these experiments, it occurred to us that one of the problems here was a size problem. In this respect, it resembles the aperture effect on the air-water interface, as you can see. I might point out that the aperture effect is not visible across the bars of the jail cell, which are microscopic in size, nor may it be visible across a wire screen, though the proportions of all the factors are proper. It must be in a model of proper size. The total force on a thin membrane stretched over a long span, it is quite easy to see, must be very much smaller than the total force over a short span.

With Dr. Brewer, a systematic study of such membranes has been undertaken. The preliminary requirement seemed to be to make apertures of the proper scale. Most of our studies, therefore, have been undertaken with protein or protein lipid complexes over a grid very much like the one in the next slide.

In general, a protein, for example, fibrinogen, is spread in a monolayer on the surface of water, under a specified lateral pressure.

An appropriate matrix, very much like this in cross-section, is pulled up through the surface of the fibrinogen, as shown here (Fig. 43). There is some associated water with the bimolecular complex, but this need not concern us.

This complex will often be stable in air, as illustrated in Fig. 44. This is a photograph of the grid covered with a bimolecular layer of fibrinogen, dried in air. The distances here are 4 μ for the wire and 12 μ for the space.

You can see that occasionally these films show certain distortions due to the stress of drying the membrane.

In an aqueous solution, which is what we are really interested in, stability seemed to be accomplished by virtue of a balance between the cohesive forces in the film and the tendency of the molecules to go into solution. The effect of scale and aperture simply bring this ratio within practical limits for many substances. In this particular arrangement, the

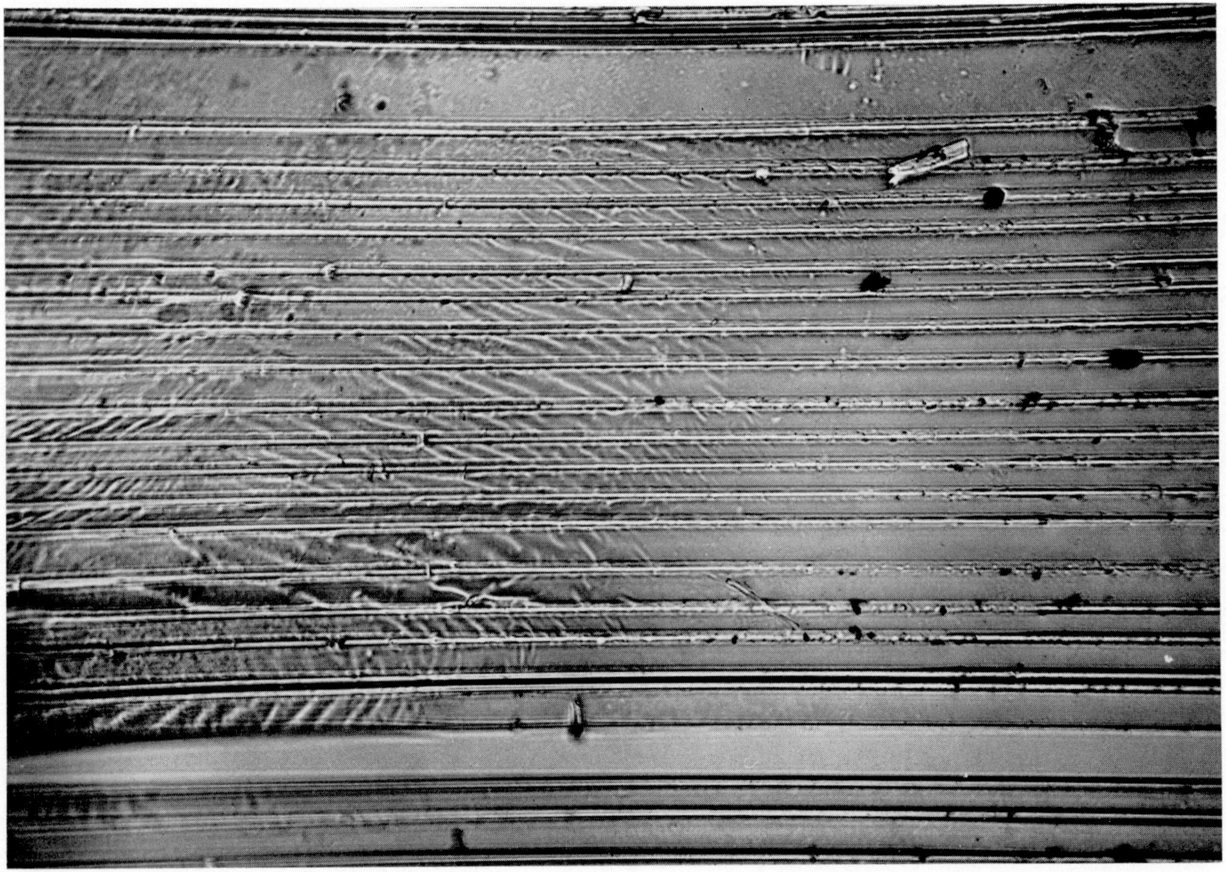

Fig. 44.

protein and protein-lipid complexes are now accessible for further study on permeability and, more particularly, for microperfusion studies.

In relating the protein films to the aperture effect, it can be seen that we really have two interfaces, back to back. The protein is analogous in solubility characteristics to the air. The association of two such interfaces seems to enhance the stability of each.

Up to this point, we have been able to make quartz fibers and grids by straightforward mechanical means. The production and handling of quartz fibers of .5 μ and up, in continuous lengths of three to five miles, has now been reduced to a routine procedure in our laboratory by specially designed instruments and techniques. A number of other mechanical techniques for working on a microscale have also been developed, but these all have failed, when structures smaller than 1 μ to 2 μ have been proposed. It is this smaller range of the size scale that most nearly approaches the scale of biological microstructures and suggests that it might offer the opportunity of setting up much more interesting complexes of proteins, lipids, and carbohydrates.

We have, therefore, been forced to develop a new set of techniques for precise isometric replication of a biological microstructure. I should like to discuss the use of one such technique in the production of membranes. This technique has allowed us to produce microstructures of an entirely different order of magnitude from that discussed earlier. The size of these structures approaches closely the estimated pore size for capillaries; whether or not this be correct need not now concern us.

The problem at hand is to make a grid or matrix with micropores of constant and measurable size. This matrix must have fixed interspaces with a critical dimension of 100 Å at least. The membrane can be produced to a dimension ranging down to 200 or 300 Å in thickness.

The technique for this is as follows. We make, first, small metal models of the inside of the intended pore or interspace. These are the exact size and shape of the intended pore. These pore models are, in turn, embedded in a plastic matrix. The plastic matrix with these embedded solid models of the pore is then sectioned at right angles to the pore axis. After this, the solid pore models are removed, leaving behind a channel or hole of appropriate size and shape in the matrix.

A brief description of each step in this procedure might make it clearer.

Though most of our studies, I might say beforehand, have been carried out with a plastic matrix, this technique allows some latitude in the selection of the physical and chemical characteristics of the membrane matrix, and we have been able to make these of glass and metal as well as of plastic.

The first step in the process is to select several thin sheets of a plastic which has the general physical and chemical properties desired (Fig.

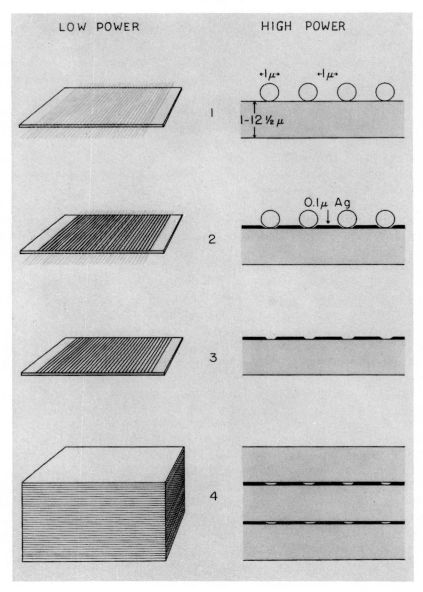

Fig. 45.

45). These are then placed under a quartz grid very much like the grid used in the preceding experiments. In this case, however, the spacing between the wires is the same as the diameter of the wires. You can see that on the cross-section at the upper right.

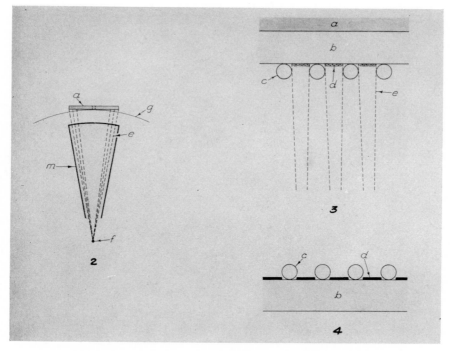

Fig. 46.

A number of these units of quartz grids and plastic sheets are next placed in a high vacuum chamber very similar to the type used for shadowing in electron microscopy.

The units are placed on the circumference of a sphere, the center of which is at a vapor source. In a high vacuum, as shown in Fig. 46, a layer of metal or salt or oxide is next evaporated onto the surface of the unit illustrated before. The evaporator beam originates at (a) and goes through a collimeter (m). The target is prepared, as you remember, by placing quartz fibers over a plastic surface. These, in effect, act as a mask, so that only between the fibers is there a deposit of the metal. The thickness of this deposit is the one element that we wish to control very closely.

These shadowed plastic sheets are then placed on top of each other as in a sandwich (Fig. 47). These are bonded together at the spaces between the metal film. After a proper bond one has solid pore models running in parallel through a solid matrix. If the matrix is of plastic, the membrane may be cut as thin as 200 to 300 Å by the glass knife microtome. The pore models are next removed, usually by chemical action, but electrolysis and heat will remove some materials, and the resulting

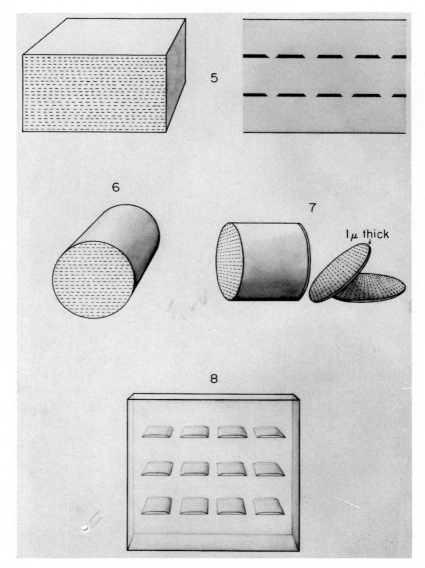

Fig. 47.

structure is now a membrane with a predetermined pore size of the order of magnitude not dissimilar to the hypothetical size of a pore in a capillary basement membrane.

These are shown in cross-section. There will be, as you see, only a very small range of variation in size of each pore. Of necessity, a number of technical details in this procedure have been omitted. However, I should like to show something of the range of the technique by some comments about these details.

As mentioned before, the matrix materials may cover a wide range. Of greatest interest to us has been the plastic monochlorotrifluoropoly-ethylene, which closely resembles Teflon in its chemical properties but is under some circumstances transparent. By a special technique, the monomer of this plastic is polymerized between each sheet of the plastic, and this gives us a good gas-free bond, which is of the same material as the rest of the membrane. It is impervious, in general, to the chemical action of almost everything except molten alkali metals.

Although uniformity of pore size is a desirable feature of this technique, it is very important also to be able to measure the pore width by some primary means. The process of making membranes allows us to make these primary measurements of pore width by measuring the thickness of the pore model. As you remember, the pore model in cross-section is now the critical width of the pore.

There is, of course, some degree of uncertainty as to whether the hole is as big as the object which filled it, but this uncertainty should be a constant factor.

If we return to the process of molecular evaporation, it can be seen in Fig. 48 that the uniformity of the deposit depends on the location of the unit area on the circumference of a sphere. I can just briefly say that the geometry of this determines the reliability of the deposit and the uniformity from target segment to target segment. This varies probably less than 1 per cent.

In practice, we put a special measuring target in this apparatus and measure the thickness of the deposit by the multiple-beam interferometer method of Tolansky. This gives us a measurement of the width of the pore to a precision of 5 plus or minus Å.

It should be apparent now that some of the characteristics of the basement membrane can be reproduced. Although studies relating the form of the isometric replicas to function are not complete, it may be of interest to show a complex structure which has a permeability for dextran molecules of 250,000 molecular weight.

Fig. 49 shows a pore model on which a monolayer of fibrinogen is stretched across the pores; (c) are the pores and (b) is the fibrinogen layer on both sides. This retards the flow of dextran molecules of larger than 250,000 molecular weight.

The order of magnitude of the aperture (c) is 1,000 Å.

It would be of interest, too, to comment that this membrane also becomes diseased. In studying it for its permeability to dextran, if plasma proteins from different individuals are exposed to the membrane, it shows a difference in permeability.

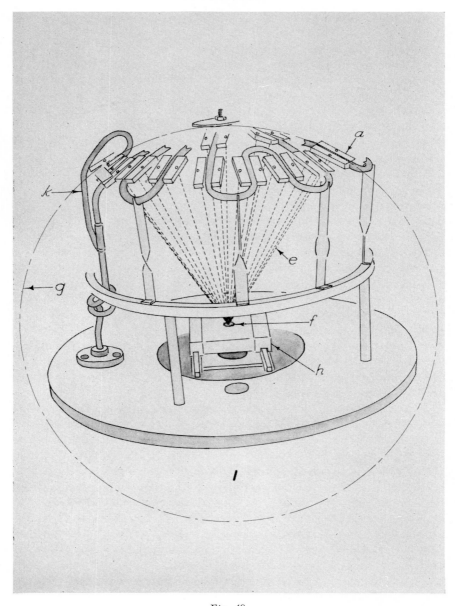

Fig. 48.

In conclusion, I would like to say that the use of isometric replicas for the study of certain physical forces bearing on the very small structures, such as pores in a membrane, etc., seems ultimately necessary for a clear understanding of these physical forces. A group of forces which pro-

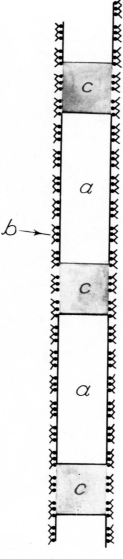

Fig. 49.

duces a stabilizing effect on an interface in a small aperture has been discussed.

A small beginning in the study of isometric replicas has been achieved. It would be impossible now to relate the present study to any biological analogue, but it is intriguing to note that several structures in the ani-

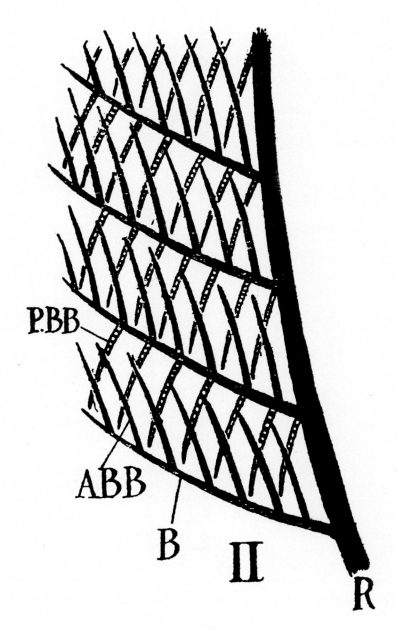

Fig. 50.

mal kingdom which are designed to act as a barrier follow this same pattern.

One example of this which is familiar to everyone is the foot processes of the podocyte in a glomerulus. Are they acting as a stabilizing matrix for the basement membrane? It would appear that their size characteristics are appropriate for this.

Fig. 50 shows a feather from a duck. Contrary to what *Life* magazine says, it is the geometry of this feather and not the chemistry of the surfaces of the feather which makes the duck float. The geometry of this is very similar to that analyzed earlier for the quartz grid fibers.

REFERENCES

1. Cassie, A. B. D., and S. Baxter. "Wettability of porous surfaces," in *Trans. Faraday Soc. 40:*546-51 (1944).
2. Danielli, J. F. Some properties of lipoid films in relation to the structure of the plasma membrane. J. cell. comp. Physiol. 7:393-408 (1935-36).
3. Langmuir, W., and D. F. Waugh. The adsorption of proteins at oil-water interface and artificial protein-lipoid membranes. J. gen. Physiol. *21:*745-55 (1937).

COMMENT

CHAIRMAN REYNOLDS: We are very grateful for this intriguing and stimulating presentation. I am sure that it must have provoked a good many unusual thoughts in people with different backgrounds.

I would like to ask Dr. Griesemer of the Department of Dermatology of the Massachusetts General Hospital to make some remarks that seem appropriate in the discussion of these papers.

DR. R. D. GRIESEMER: While much of our work (1, 2, 3, 4) on the permeation of chemical substances through skin is not directly related to the subjects discussed today, one or two ideas may apply to the problems of capillary permeability.

Fig. 51 shows the kind of structure we are studying in skin. This is a diagram of the barrier layer in the human epidermis. The barrier we are concerned with is the darker-lined horizontal area lying between the stratum corneum and stratum granulosum. It is only 10 μ thick, yet it is remarkably impermeable to many substances.

Life is dependent on the continuity of this barrier, for when it is defective severe problems arise. In burns the barrier is disrupted and tissue fluids are lost freely; the patient may go into shock and die. When the barrier is broken by any means, microorganisms and toxic substances are free to enter the body and wreak destruction. It is easy to see that the chief function of the skin is to manufacture and maintain this barrier and re-form it when it is destroyed. There is good evidence to indicate that the barrier is re-formed within 24 to 48 hours if the defect is small,

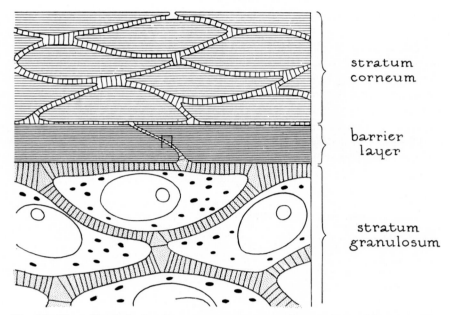

Fig. 51. The cells of the barrier are more compact and more closely bound together than are those of the stratum corneum. The intercellular spaces are smallest in the barrier and largest in the living epidermis beneath. In the stratum corneum, the intercellular spaces increase in size as the cells separate and fall away into the external environment. The small rectangular area in the barrier is shown in higher magnification in Fig. 52.

e.g., that produced by a pinprick. In this sense the barrier is a dynamic membrane.

The function of the skin differs from that of the capillary wall. It is to maintain impermeability, rather than selective permeability, which is required of the capillary wall. While the epidermal barrier may prove to be constructed in an entirely different manner from the capillary wall, the same physical and chemical factors probably govern the permeability of both membranes.

Let us consider the fine structure of the barrier, as shown in a diagram of an electron microscope picture taken from a paper by Dr. Selby(5) (Fig. 52). The junction between two epidermal cells in the barrier layer is represented. A molecule may penetrate the barrier by passing through the cells, through the spaces between the cells, or through both cells and spaces.

In the center of the desmosomes (bridges between the cells) the cell membranes are separated by a space which is about 200 Å thick and filled with electron-dense material. Between the bridges, empty spaces are visible in the electron microscope picture. Whether they are arti-

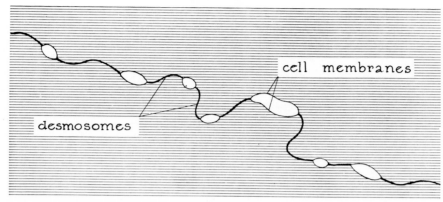

Fig. 52. Diagram of cellular junction in barrier layer, taken from electron-microscopic photograph in Fig. 11 of Selby's paper(5). Desmosomes, or intercellular bridges, are not continuous from cell to cell; well-defined cell membranes cross the center of each bridge. Between adjacent desmosomes the cell membranes have retracted, leaving intercellular spaces. These spaces have no electron density; they may be artifacts; electron-dense material present in life may have been lost during preparation of tissue for electron microscopy.

facts or are present in life is unknown. If they are real, they must be filled with material both fluid and solid in nature. It is reasonable to suppose that penetrating molecules would find an easier path through this material than through the compact dead cells nearby.

The size of these intercellular spaces is about one micron, falling within the range of the artificial membrane pores just described by Dr. Arnold. Since the diameter of these spaces is much larger than the molecular dimensions of most penetrating substances, the chief resistance to penetration is the force of molecular interaction between the penetrating substances and the lining and contents of the spaces. This charge effect is the most important factor governing the penetration of small molecules (up to 200 to 300 molecular weight) through the skin. Larger molecules do not penetrate in significant amounts.

Because of its small size, the water molecule passes more readily through the skin than do other substances. Permeability studies on a series of substances of nearly similar molecular weight, reported by Treherne(6), show that the ether/water partition coefficient of a substance is correlated with its rate of penetration through the skin: the higher the ether solubility, the more rapid is its rate of penetration. This indicates that non-polar groups must form part of the lining and contents of the pores in the skin barrier.

However, Cullumbine(7) has shown in unpublished studies that as the ether/water partition coefficient rises, permeability reaches a maximum when the coefficient is one, i.e., when the substance is equally soluble in polar and non-polar solvents. As the coefficient increases above one, the permeability declines. This indicates that pore lining and contents in the skin barrier contain both polar and non-polar groups. Therefore, a complex fine structure must exist in the skin barrier; perhaps some of its features may be present also in the capillary wall.

CHAIRMAN REYNOLDS: I would like to expose our panel to any pertinent questions you may have, until, if you wish, five-thirty. I believe that there may be one or two pertinent questions. Please address your question to a specific member of the panel. Dr. Mayerson, do you have something to say?

DR. MAYERSON: I don't have any questions. I wanted to make several comments. Referring to Dr. Renkin's talk, I would like to re-emphasize that what he has said refers to muscle, and it is just as Chester Hyman said to me a while ago, that "man cannot live by muscle alone." In other words, I would like to point out that where other areas in the body have been studied, the situation is not quite as simple as the picture in muscle would make it appear.

I would subscribe to everything that Dr. Renkin and Dr. Pappenheimer have shown about muscle, but when we start studying the intestine and the intestinal capillaries and the liver capillaries, there we find a different situation. We find that the pores are probably different sizes. Grotte at Upsala, who has done work similar to ours, calls these "leaks." We prefer to say that there are big pores and little pores.

At any rate, I should like to suggest that the pores are not all the same size. Certainly, capillaries of different parts of the body leak in different ways, so that we find different amounts of protein in lymph draining these areas. In our experiments with dextran fractions of different molecular weights, we haven't gotten up to a big enough molecule, even though we have worked to 412,000 average molecular weight, which will stay in the liver capillary and really stay in. They all come through.

I would like to make this point, and this is late in the afternoon to be making these points—that we find that we can vary the pore size by distending the vascular system. We think we can stretch pores.

I had hoped that, perhaps, Dr. Moore would tell us that these pores will open up, but since we haven't been shown the pores, I don't know that we can have them open up.

Referring to Dr. Sapirstein's work, although it sounded quite unorthodox, we have felt for a long time that we must postulate a pericapillary space, for this reason: when we put a tagged albumin (radioactive iodinated albumin) into the plasma and then follow it through the lymph, we get two different types of curves; that is, in the plasma we get the usual decay type of curve that we would expect, where it falls off semilogarithmically. On the other hand, in the lymph, we get a growth curve.

This can be explained, as far as we can see it, only by postulating a pericapillary space; so that the protein goes in there and mixes before we can pick it up in lymph.

CHAIRMAN REYNOLDS: Dr. Renkin, would you care to make any comments at this time?

DR. RENKIN: I agree with Dr. Mayerson completely. If I failed to emphasize that the data of Pappenheimer and his co-workers which I showed in Table 1 were taken under specific conditions on one particular tissue, then I apologize for it. They represent the capillaries in resting mammalian skeletal muscle, and I think that every other tissue which has capillaries in it ought to be investigated on its own merits.

CHAIRMAN REYNOLDS: Dr. Fawcett, would you care to comment on this pericapillary stuff that the physiologists are talking about?

DR. FAWCETT: I have no comment to make on that. I see no barrier. Of course, the barrier postulated is that of the ground substance, and I am quite sure that its solubilities are such that we lose it through fixation. It may be related chemically in its composition to the basement membrane material that I spoke of, but that we do seem to succeed in retaining, whereas the general ground substance of the connective tissue just melts away; so we are not in a position to say where that barrier is. We can't see it.

CHAIRMAN REYNOLDS: Do you visualize the possibility that, maybe, some ingenious fellow will come along someday and be able to do this with something that you can get hold of and see?

DR. FAWCETT: I hope, someday we will get a greater variety of fixing agents, some which may preserve some of those things which we now lose, such as osmium.

DR. REYNOLDS: Are there any further questions or comments that anyone cares to make?

DR. PALADE: I would like to ask how big should a pore be to allow passage of a molecular moiety?

CHAIRMAN REYNOLDS: To whom is your question directed?

DR. PALADE: To Dr. Renkin.

CHAIRMAN REYNOLDS: May I ask you to repeat it, first, Dr. Palade, because I don't think that the people in the back could hear?

DR. PALADE: How large is the diameter of a pore allowing the passage of a molecule of ferritin?

DR. RENKIN: Could I ask what, approximately, the size of a molecule of ferritin is?

DR. PALADE: Ninety-three Å.

DR. RENKIN: The average pore size as calculated from the data on small molecules comes out to be about 3 Å in radius. Is your figure in radius?

DR. PALADE: No, it is diameter.

Dr. Renkin: My figure would be 60 in diameter. But this represents an average figure, measured on the basis of capillary permeability to small molecules which penetrate with little restriction. In Table 1, per- meability of the capillaries to hemoglobin, which has a radius of 31 Å, was written down as zero. What this zero means is "too small to detect by the methods used." There is no doubt that in lymph collected from skeletal muscle at rest, appreciable quantities of serum albumin appear; serum globulins appear too, and since the lymph clots, fibrinogen is also present. All I can say is that the total area of pores much greater than 30 Å in radius must be less than 1 per cent of the total pore area. This does not mean that this small fraction of 1 per cent is of little impor- tance, because through this small percentage of large pores a very important quantity of material must pass.

Independent evidence tells us that there must be some pores big enough to let serum globulins out, and there must be some pores large enough to let ferritin out. We do not know what the upper limit of pore size is, but I think it would be safe to say that these large pores make up less than 1 per cent of the total pore area.

Dr. Palade: What is particularly disturbing for this assumption is that there are stable pores of given sizes, including up to, let's say, 100 or 200 Å to allow ferritin molecules to go through. Isn't it a fact that pores of this size should be clearly visible in the electron microscope, and you can see the ferritin molecules in transit through the various layers of the capillary wall and no pores either before or behind them?

Dr. Zweifach: Where does vesiculation begin and phagocytosis end, or vice versa, here? How do you know that ferritin is passing through by permeation in the same method that water does?

Dr. Palade: By the difference between phagocytosis and vesiculation artificially; the same basic mechanism.

Chairman Reynolds: Dr. Arnold, do you have a comment?

Dr. Arnold: This is one of the questions we set out to answer, but I I am not sure that I have the complete answer to it. The problem is very complex. One can have a monomolecular membrane stretched across a space, which we are calling a pore, that is able to refuse admittance to a large molecule like dextran. In cross-section this membrane is not visible to the electron microscopist. We tried to fix and look at some bimolecular layers and we lost them by the techniques of osmic acid fixation. Yet they are a perfectly good barrier to the movement of large molecules.

There are some other data in the literature, of course, to suggest that we have been very naïve about our concept of the mechanism of trans- port of large molecules across these things called pores. The diffusion across many porous minerals does not fit well with the known size of the pore. There are diffusion studies of large molecules across pore areas which probably give us no good idea as to the real geometry and size of the pore.

CHAIRMAN REYNOLDS: There is time for one further comment. Does anyone on the panel wish to make a concluding remark?

DR. MOORE: I would like to make it clear—we had quite a little discussion a moment ago—that I did not intend to say that vesicles were the primary means of transporting material across capillary walls. I am sure that most people will probably go away with this impression. But all I intended to do was to show what the electron micrograph shows. Essentially, I don't understand what is going on, but I think that we might orient our thinking a little bit in the light of what is seen in the electron microscope. For a number of years, we have been thinking about pores because it is easy to imagine membranes. Well, it turns out that not always in biology does nature pick out the system that the mind most readily imagines.

I think, if we would simply be willing to throw away our old concepts entirely, both the anatomists and the physiologists, and try to pick up some new concepts and put all the things together, probably we are going to have to stop talking about this simple membrane with holes in it.

CHAIRMAN REYNOLDS: I think, on this note, we should probably conclude our deliberations this afternoon.

REFERENCES

1. Blank, I. H., R. D. Griesemer, and E. Gould. The penetration of an anticholinesterase agent (sarin) into skin. I. Rate of penetration into excised human skin. J. invest. Derm. 29:299-309 (1957).
2. Blank, I. H., R. D. Griesemer, and E. Gould. The penetration of an anticholinesterase agent (sarin) into skin. II. Autoradiographie studies. J. invest. Derm. 30:187-91 (1958).
3. Griesemer, R. D., I. H. Blank, and E. Gould. The penetration of an anticholinesterase agent (sarin) into skin. III. A method for studying the rate of penetration into the skin of the living rabbit. J. invest. Derm. Accepted for publication.
4. Griesemer, R. D. Protection against the transfer of matter through the skin. Symposium on the Human Integument-Normal and Abnormal. Indianapolis: December 28, 1957.
5. Selby, C. C. An electromicroscopic study of thin sections of human skin. II. Superficial cell layers of footpad epidermis. J. invest. Derm. 29:131-50 (1957).
6. Treherne, J. E. The permeability of skin to some non-electrolytes. J. Physiol. 133:171-80 (1956).
7. Cullumbine, H. Personal communication.

[The conference adjourned at five-thirty o'clock.]

April 1, 1958

The Fifth Conference on Microcirculatory Physiology and Pathology convened on Tuesday morning, April 1, 1958, in the Empire State Room of the Hotel Statler, Buffalo, New York, at 9:30 A.M., Dr. S. R. M. Reynolds, University of Illinois College of Medicine, presiding.

Dr. S. R. M. Reynolds: Ladies and Gentlemen: It is 9:30 and I think that we should start the proceedings of the day. The meeting this morning, as you can see from the program, is given over to a series of presentations by individuals, some members of our conference and some not. This begins the Fifth Microcirculatory Conference, which I hope, will reach its peak this afternoon in the symposium which has been planned for you.

I am going to preside this morning only to start the activities and then turn the program over to the new Chairman of the Microcirculatory Conference, who is Dr. Edmund P. Fowler, Jr., of Columbia University. This is a departure from our usual procedure, because it became clear to the Executive Committee from past experience that it is a good idea for the members of the Microcirculatory Conference to see and know the chairman who is going to be doing the work next year. When he writes to some of you to ask for help or participation in planning the presentations for meetings, you will know who he is and he won't be just another name, as may have been the case in times past.

I am going to turn the program, therefore, over to Dr. Fowler, who will conduct it this morning. Dr. Fowler, I will ask you to come up and take over.

Chairman Fowler: Thank you, Dr. Reynolds. I would like to introduce Dr. Jørn Ditzel, whose qualifications and affiliations are listed in the program. He will talk to you on "The Relationship in Diabetes Mellitus of Abnormal Vasomotor Patterns in the Smaller Blood Vessels to Retinopathy and Nephropathy."

The Relationship in Diabetes Mellitus of Abnormal Vasomotor Patterns in the Smaller Blood Vessels to Retinopathy and Nephropathy

Jørn Ditzel

Baker Clinic Research Laboratory, New England Deaconess Hospital, the Joslin Clinic and Department of Medicine, Harvard University Medical School

The rising incidence of retinopathy and intercapillary glomerulosclerosis, the specific venous capillary disease in long-term diabetes, is a challenging problem.

Besides the retina, the bulbar conjunctiva is the only place in which detailed observations of the smaller blood vessels can be made *in vivo*. While only the larger arterioles and venules are observable in the retina, the biomicroscope adapted to the bulbar conjunctiva makes the terminal arterioles, capillaries, smaller venules, and the blood flow within them visible. In order to learn more about the behavior of the terminal vascular bed in diabetes, the smaller blood vessels of the bulbar conjunctiva were examined in more than 1,000 diabetic and non-diabetic healthy persons. In the diabetic subjects two vasomotor patterns could be distinguished which differed from the normal pattern present in healthy persons. The abnormal vascular patterns designated Vascular Pattern-Change I and Vascular Pattern-Change II were characterized by respectively decreased and increased vasomotor tone and both led to slowing of blood flow, stasis, and exudation through the venous part of the capillaries and the venules. Vascular Pattern-Change I, characterized by venular dilatation (loss of tone), was reversible and improved in some cases with long-term optimal control. Similar short-term reversions of venular congestion occasionally occurred during the day. The venular dilatation was, as a rule, least marked in the later afternoon at the time when dietary intake and insulin effect might be expected to produce the optimal daily metabolic pattern (Proc. Soc. Exp. Biol. and Med. 97:475, 1958).

A study of the vascular response patterns observed microscopically in the bulbar conjunctiva was made in 60 young diabetics with retinopathy and nephropathy. A significant relationship was found between the conjunctival pattern abnormality and the extent of small blood vessel degeneration. This suggests that abnormal vasomotor changes in the retinal and glomerular vessels play an important role in the development of diabetic retinopathy and glomerulosclerosis.[1]

DISCUSSION

CHAIRMAN FOWLER: Dr. Ditzel's paper is now open for general discussion. Is there any discussion from the floor?

DR. MELVIN H. KNISELY (Medical College of South Carolina): I would rather not have been the first, but Dr. Ditzel showed changes in the diameters of the veins, the ratio of the arteries to the veins, and I was curious to know if he had thought a little about whether there are changes in the artery between the treated and the untreated. Are most of the changes in the vein or are there some measurable changes in the artery? That is my question.

Then, I'll try not to make a speech, but the tissue culture people know particularly which substances are necessary to nourish a certain strain of cells, and the bacteriologist can tell you exactly which substances are necessary to nourish a certain strain of bacteria—amino acids, sugars, and so on. It seems to me that one of the great problems in understanding the vasculature in health and disease consists, for the future, of trying to know exactly which molecules are necessary for the nourishment of endothelium so that it does not bleed, and at what rates must these molecules arrive, the diabetes being a special case.

In the positions where you showed the extra fluidity outside the vessels, which then disappeared, there are circumstances where all you have to do is slow down the blood flow, and then all the vessels will begin to leak and you have extravascular fluid. Speed it up again and bring the molecules in for nourishment fast enough, and then the vessels stop leaking.

Of course, there are other factors here, too, certainly, but I think that this is such a simple one that you will have to keep it in mind to find out how much of the whole phenomenon is a part of it.

To recapitulate, did the arteries change diameters before treatment, and what do we know about the problem of what substance is necessary for nourishment of the endothelium, and about the losses due merely to rates of flow.

DR. ROBERT LANDESMAN (Cornell University Medical College): I must congratulate the speaker on his beautiful pictures of the conjunctival

---

[1] The abstract which is printed here was prepared by Dr. Jørn Ditzel. The full paper, of which he was co-author, was published in the May, 1958, issue of American Medical Association Arch. Int. Med. *101*:912, under the title "The Relationship of Abnormal Vascular Responses to Retinopathy and Nephropathy in Diabetics."

vasculature. We have been studying these same vessels primarily in pregnancy and also in the diabetic. We have been impressed concerning the process of ischemia that occurs in the diabetic and also the marked constriction of the terminal arterioles in this disease.

However, we have not been able to confirm the speaker's marked dilatation of the venular system associated with the non-treatment of diabetes, and we have not been able to find any of these exudative processes in the conjunctiva. I would like to ask the speaker concerning the method of taking these pictures, the type of film, and the type of lighting.

DR. B. W. ZWEIFACH (New York University-Bellevue Medical Center): I think it is of some interest to note that in the diabetic syndrome the arterioles are constricted under conditions where the venular system or collecting venule is dilated—and this, in turn, is associated with capillary ischemia. This vasomotor pattern is unusual, when compared with conventional types of ischemia produced by hypotension, vasoconstrictor drugs, or by stimulation of the sympathetic nervous system. Under these conditions, an ischemia develops primarily by virtue of a closure of the parent feeding arterioles, resulting in a decreased blood flow through the capillary system, and an accompanying reduction in the total blood circulating through the venules. Does Dr. Ditzel feel that we are dealing here, not only with the problem of increased vasomotor tone producing the accompanying ischemia, but also with some type of venular damage, and possibly changes in the aggregation of red cells, a phenomenon akin to what has been called "sludging"?

CHAIRMAN FOWLER: Is anybody impelled to ask another question at this time?

DR. MELVIN KNISELY: On this problem of whether or not the arteries shut off, you get quite large changes in the contraction of arteries merely by changing the blood volume. If you go to the blood bank and watch them bleed people, as the volume goes down, many arteries are shut off. Therefore, two sets of data exist which agree quite a bit, perhaps only because of the different blood volumes of patients.

CHAIRMAN FOWLER: The Chair would like to ask the speaker whether he watched these vessels over a considerable period, and what were the standard deviations in the kind of dilation and description described. One can get quite marked changes of blood flow without visible changes in diameter.

DR. DITZEL: Dr. Knisely, the changes in the venules are much more obvious than those in the arterioles. Sometimes a constriction can be seen in the arterioles accompanying the venular dilation, but often the arteriolar change is not measurable. But what is happening at a place beyond the microscopic field observed, we don't know. It might be that the venular dilation is a consequence of a spasm in the arterioles, or a consequence of a slow blood flow leading to a loss of tone in the collecting venules.

Thank you for your kind comment, Dr. Landesman. The easiest thing I can do is refer you to the publication by St. Clair and myself on the method of photographing the smaller blood vessels in human subjects (*Circulation* 10:277, 1954). The best pictures were obtained by using Kodak Panatomic X film and a high-speed electronic flash.

I know about your papers concerning the changes in the bulbar conjunctiva vascular bed during pregnancy. I think we agree very much on the point that ischemia with marked constriction of the terminal arterioles is a dominant feature in diabetics late in the third trimester (see "The responses of the smaller blood vessels and the serum proteins in pregnant diabetic subjects," *Diabetes* 6:307, 1957). The venular dilation is observable only in some and not all severe non-pregnant diabetics or pregnant diabetics when studied early during pregnancy, i.e., first trimester. For demonstrating these changes, routine microphotography is necessary.

Yes, Dr. Zweifach, the changes in the peripheral vascular bed during many acute diseases, and not only in diabetes, are characterized by changes in the caliber of the venules which are not parallel and thus passive of those changes taking place in the arterioles (see E. H. Bloch, "*In vivo* microscopic observations of the circulating blood in acute myocardial infarction," *Amer. J. med. Sci.* 229:280-93, 1955).

Your second question, I guess, should be understood to ask whether I understand the "aggregation of the red cells" to be identical with sludging or agglutination of the red cells.

Here my answer would be yes. In my opinion, the term "agglutination" should be used only to describe an irreversible clumping of red cells, e.g., ischemoagglutination. The term "sludging" has come to mean so many things, such as stasis, slow blood flow, and flow containing blood clumps, that I prefer the expression "aggregation." The diabetic condition, when out of control, is characterized by changes in the plasma proteins, lipoproteins, and carbohydrates containing proteins. These substances, being colloids, increase the tendency of the red cells to aggregate. In diabetics of long standing the intravascular erythrocyte aggregation is very pronounced.

Dr. Fowler, every observation made included microphotographs of the vessels. We have studied about 200 healthy young individuals at various times during the day. Practically always we have found no, or little, change in the diameter of the larger arterioles and collecting venules. Nothing can be said about the capillaries because most of them cannot be observed with this technique. Heat and mechanical trauma and irritation lead to a general parallel dilation of both arterioles and venules and can, therefore, most often be differentiated from the changes occurring in response to acute diseases. The changes in the young diabetics were significantly different from those occurring in healthy young individuals.

CHAIRMAN FOWLER: The next presentation is by Dr. John W. Irwin, who will show us some moving pictures of anaphylaxis in animals.

The Pulmonary Microcirculation of Living Rabbits During Passive Anaphylaxis

John W. Irwin, Sandylee Weille, Irene M. York, Mitchell A. Rappaport

Microcirculatory Laboratory, Massachusetts Eye and Ear Infirmary

Burrage *et al.*(1, 2) observed "hyaline" emboli in the microscopic vessels of living rabbits during active anaphylaxis as well as during histamine shock. Germuth and McKinnon(3) with histological methods showed numerous amorphous hyaline and granular thrombi plugging alveolar capillaries of normal guinea pigs injected with soluble antigen-antibody complexes.

METHODS

Each of four toe pads of rabbits was injected with .02 ml. Freund's adjuvant which contained 15 to 25 mg. bovine serum albumin per ml. emulsion. After an interval of 2 to 3 weeks, booster intravenous injections of 5 to 10 mg. bovine serum albumin per ml. saline were given. Seven days later rabbits were bled and serum pooled. The amount of antibody nitrogen per milliliter of this serum was determined with the use of a Beckman spectrophotometer. Twenty-four to forty-eight hours before the experiments, normal rabbits were injected intravenously with this pooled serum on the basis of known amount of antibody nitrogen.

Detailed accounts of techniques of exposing the lung of living rabbits and maintaining the lung quiet (no respiratory movements) have been given by Irwin *et al.*(4).

After the lung of a sensitized animal was exposed and placed under microscopic observation, a known amount of antigen nitrogen (bovine albumin) was given intravenously. Ratio of antibody nitrogen to antigen nitrogen varied from 1:1 to 200:1 and from 1:1 to 1:60. Various ratios have been used, and more than 400 experiments have been done.

RESULTS

Death occurred in 27 animals within 10 minutes of the shocking dose of antigen. Changes noted in the microscopic pulmonary blood vessels of all 27 included blocking of arterioles, capillaries, and venules with "hyaline" emboli as well as constriction of pulmonary arterioles and

This study was supported by grants from the National Tuberculosis Association.

venules. Hyaline emboli and constriction without death were noted in the microscopic pulmonary vessels of 33 other animals. Emboli alone and no death were seen in 14 other animals, and constriction alone in 8 others. Fig. 53A shows a pulmonary arteriole before the anaphylaxis and Fig. 53B the same vessel with a hyaline embolus in its lumen after the shocking dose. Fig. 54A shows a pulmonary arteriole before anaphylaxis, and Fig. 54B shows the narrowed lumen of this same vessel during anaphylaxis.

DISCUSSION

It is obvious that passive anaphylaxis leading to rapid death is most uncertain in the rabbit, in contrast to the guinea pig. To date it has not been possible to determine the optimal ratio of antibody nitrogen to antigen nitrogen.

Of interest is the fact that death on the basis of anaphylaxis has not been observed unless "hyaline" emboli within the small pulmonary vessels and constriction of pulmonary arterioles and venules were noted. It is entirely possible that these emboli and constriction of these small pulmonary vessels may be important in anaphylactic death.

Study of the composition of the hyaline emboli has not been undertaken. Four hypotheses appear feasible: (1) antigen-antibody complexes, (2) platelet emboli, (3) white blood cell emboli, and (4) altered proteins. Against these "hyaline" emboli being antigen-antibody complexes are the observations of Burrage et al.(2) that similar "hyaline" emboli were seen during histamine shock.

RESULTS

1. "Hyaline" emboli and constriction of small pulmonary blood vessels were noted during passive anaphylaxis leading to death.

2. These emboli and constriction have been noted in shocked animals which did not die immediately because of passive anaphylaxis.

REFERENCES

1. Burrage, W. S., and J. W. Irwin. Microscopic observations of the pulmonary arterioles, capillaries, and venules of living mammals before and during anaphylaxis. J. Allergy. 24:289-96 (1953).
2. Burrage, W. S., J. W. Irwin, J. I. Gallemore, and D. M. K. Wang. Effects of histamine and epinephrine on the small pulmonary blood vessels of living rabbits. J. Allergy. 25:293-301 (1954).
3. Germuth, F. G., and G. E. McKinnon. Studies on the biological properties of antigen-antibody complexes. I. Anaphylactic shock induced by soluble antigen-antibody complexes in unsensitized normal guinea pigs. Bull. Johns Hopkins Hosp. 101:13-44 (1957).
4. Irwin, J. W., W. S. Burrage, C. E. Aimar, and R. W. Chesnut, Jr. Microscopical observations of the pulmonary arterioles, capillaries, and venules of living guinea pigs and rabbits. Anat. Rec. 119:391-408 (1954).

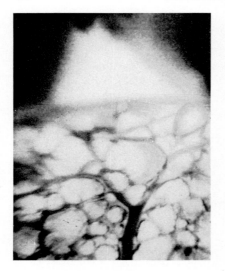

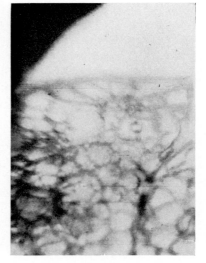

Fig. 53a.   Fig. 53b.

Discussion

CHAIRMAN FOWLER: This paper is now open for discussion. Are there any questions or comments?

DR. WILLIAM H. KNISELY (Duke University): Dr. Irwin and I have discussed this business of emboli formation in anaphylaxis for the past several years. I want to put into the record some things that I think are worth mentioning.

I have had two students work on this problem for bachelor's degrees in medicine. They carried out essentially the sensitization procedure which Dr. Irwin performed previously in active anaphylaxis(1). However, in some animals the shocking antigen was added intra-arterially and in others intravenously, and arterial and venous pressures were measured. The assumption was that if emboli were formed, they would embolize at different locations in the two groups, and if one area embolized were a non-vital location this might separate categories of animals on the basis of fatality as an endpoint. This did occur. This work was done with the help of Mr. Allen Thorne(2).

Another student, Mr. Andrew Wallace, worked on the problem of anaphylaxis with several preparations(3), one similar to the one which Dr. Irwin used(1), and another similar to that which Dr. Drinker used back in 1924(4). Drinker measured pulmonary artery pressures during anaphylaxis, and to do this he split the sternum, opened the pericardium, and cannulated the main pulmonary artery while the animal continued

Fig. 54a.

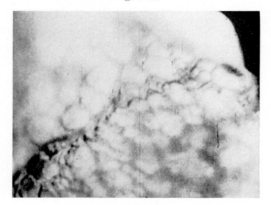

Fig. 54b.

to breathe on its own because the pleural sacs remained intact. Wallace used this preparation and observed the large pulmonary vessels during anaphylaxis, as well as observing the other end of the stream, the small vessels on the edge of the lung, microscopically in other animals, as had Burrage and Irwin.

With these preparations we have frequently seen active anaphylaxis without constriction, but always with the presence of emboli; and, with the preparation with the sternum split and the major pulmonary arteries visible, we have seen that the major pulmonary arteries do not constrict during anaphylaxis, but rather they go from a vessel of about 3 to 5 mm. in diameter to one of several centimeters in diameter. You will remember —I know that Dr. Irwin does—that Grove(5) showed that in *in vitro* experiments, strips cut from the major pulmonary artery constrict when antigen is added to the bath. These experiments have been considered strong support for the concept of arterial constriction as the cause of death in anaphylaxis. All we can say from the experiments carried out by Andrew Wallace is that if the major artery constricts during anaphylaxis, it does not get smaller, but rather gets bigger. John, I did not see any constriction today in passive anaphylaxis. I want to ask you specifically, did you see constriction in passive anaphylaxis?

DR. ZWEIFACH: There are two questions that I would like to ask. Do you mean to imply that antigen-antibody reactions of this sort introduce a set of pathology which runs its course simply on the basis of embolization? It is well known that antigen-antibody reactions, particularly of the active anaphylactic type, involve parenchymal damage to organs, such as the kidney and adrenals, in addition to the lung. Also, as shown by Ovary and Briot (1951) in what they call passive cutaneous anaphylaxis, the introduction of an antibody locally, followed by an appropriate antigen systemically, produces endothelial damage.

An integral part of the antigen-antibody reaction seems to involve widespread endothelial damage, albeit to a greater extent in some organs which are more susceptible than others. Do you consider this to be a part of the physical effects of multiple thrombi, or may this not represent a separate entity?

Various workers have suggested that the antigen-antibody reaction involves some component of the hemostatic system, possibly a protein component such as fibrinogen, which lines the blood vessels. Does this appear to be a reasonable suggestion on the basis of your observations in the lung?

DR. MELVIN KNISELY: I had the privilege of studying immunology a long time ago under a student of Paul Ehrlich's. I have lost the specific meanings of active and passive anaphylaxis; I have a suspicious mind and, perhaps, the rest of you have too.

Offhand, let me ask this question: does this mean in one case that you have the substances reacting with each other, and then put them into the vascular system, as you put them into the test tube, and, perhaps, in the other case, you have substances in the animal which can react with the whole animal, in various parts, so you have much more than just a test tube reaction? Is that one possibility here?

The other thing that I wanted to say on embolization is, our laboratory has been studying the physics of the flow of substances and, in general, our generation of mankind and all past talk about blood as though it were a fluid, which it is not. It is a mixture of things. Part of the resistance to flow is the rubbing together of solids and part is the deformation of solids. Those lung vessels are segments of cones, and it is possible that the stuff you have there is a Bigham body, which has the physics of toothpaste. You take a tube of toothpaste and begin to squeeze on it and no flow starts. When you get the pressure up to a certain point, the flow starts. As you reduce the pressure slowly, the flow stops, while you still have a pressure.

If this is a Bigham body—and it looked very much like it—and if those vessels are cones, it would be perfectly possible to stop the forward flow without ever having any single one of those big pieces go from one wall to the other. The whole thing would stop when you have a positive pressure against it. That could easily explain the stopping up here and the increased diameters of the stems of those vessels.

CHAIRMAN FOWLER: I should like to ask Dr. Irwin where he thinks the emboli that he showed come from? Do they develop locally in the lung or are they from elsewhere in the body?

DR. IRWIN: In answer to the first question by Dr. William Knisely, we didn't continue the film because time was running out, and I am building this film for another purpose. The next scenes would have shown you the constriction, so it is present. We have shown you before, in a previous meeting, that it is present in active anaphylaxis. It can disappear completely.

Dr. Zweifach has asked the question as to whether other organs were injured. Similar emboli have been observed in the small blood vessels of the liver during anaphylaxis. In the blood vessels of the bulbar conjunctiva of human beings having asthma due to an antigen-antibody reaction, we have noted similar-appearing emboli.

DR. ZWEIFACH: One can produce, for example, extensive glomerular damage without concomitant embolization.

DR. IRWIN: Well, not necessarily. It would not be possible to state that there is or is not endothelial damage, because even under the best conditions we cannot see endothelial cells of the blood vessels well.

DR. ZWEIFACH: A simple way of following endothelial damage would be to introduce carbon into the blood stream. The circulating carbon shows a marked propensity to adhere to injured areas. In the base of an antibody-antigen reaction in the mouse or rabbit, the deposition of particulate matter as an index of injury can be followed under the microscope. Masses of carbon are found adhering to the vessels of the glomeruli of the kidney, in the adrenal and the lung, in addition to the usual sequestration by the reticulo-endothelial elements of the liver and spleen.

DR. IRWIN: Yes, it could be. I wouldn't argue that point.

DR. ZWEIFACH: The fact that the antibody-antigen reaction can be altered (as demonstrated in the recent British literature) by pretreating animals with histamine releasers, would seem to argue for the participation of vasoactive amines in the embolization phenomenon.

DR. IRWIN: That is what I pointed out at the beginning. Some now feel that serotonin is very important in anaphylaxis. In the past, histamine was the big factor. Neither one explains the whole problem. It would be convenient to have one factor explaining immunology, but such is not the case as yet. Everybody would like to find one substance, the so-called X substance, to explain everything in immunology, but we haven't hit this level yet, certainly.

In regard to Dr. Knisely's question, as between active and passive anaphylaxis, in active anaphylaxis you put the antigen in several days before, usually 21, roughly, and let the animal build its own antibody, and then you reintroduce the antigen at this point and shock the animal, whereas, in passive anaphylaxis you put your antibody, which you have made in another animal, into the animal, and then you can quickly follow it with antigen any time you so desire, within, say, 24 hours or 48 hours.

DR. MELVIN KNISELY: Maybe the vasculature processes follow.

DR. IRWIN: That's right, but we saw no difference. As far as these embolization and constriction processes are concerned, there is no difference between active and passive anaphylaxis. This is the only point I was trying to make.

DR. DITZEL: What is the substance in, white cells or proteins?

DR. IRWIN: I don't know.

DR. DITZEL: That should be easy to find out.

DR. IRWIN: It is not so easy because one must secure one of these emboli from a small blood vessel while the animal is still living. Dr. Germuth, in a series of papers in the Bulletin of the Johns Hopkins Hospital during 1957 (3 above) has presented evidence that these emboli are antigen-antibody complexes. These are good papers, but to date, his evidence is far from complete.

DR. ZWEIFACH: It might be possible to label them with Coon's fluorescent technique.

DR. MELVIN KNISELY: Is there any reason to exclude the idea that they may be formed throughout the circulation rather than continuously?

DR. IRWIN: I think that is the answer. Every place we have looked, we have found them. You would have to go through an animal systemically, and that, as you know, would take a matter of years.

CHAIRMAN FOWLER: The next presentation is by Dr. William Knisely and Dr. Mahaley from the Departments of Anatomy and Medicine of Duke University. Dr. Knisely will give the presentation.

REFERENCES

1. Burrage, W. S., and J. W. Irwin. Microscopic observations of the pulmonary arterioles, capillaries, and venules of living mammals before and during anaphylaxis. J. Allergy. 24:289-96 (1953).
2. Thorne, N. A. A comparison of responses of sensitized rabbits to challenging doses of antigen via intravenous and intra-arterial injection routes.

Thesis for bachelor's degree in medicine. Duke University (1957). On loan from Duke University Library.

3. Wallace, A. G. Evidence in support of the hypothesis that pulmonary embolization is a major factor in fatal experimental anaphylactic shock in rabbits. Thesis for bachelor's degree in medicine. Duke University (1958). On loan from Duke University Library.

4. Drinker, C. K., and J. Bronfenbrenner. The pulmonary circulation in anaphylaxis. J. Immunol. 9:387-406 (1924).

5. Grove, E. F. Studies in anaphylaxis in the rabbit (sec. 5). J. Immunol. 23:147-52 (1932).

Relations Between Size and Distribution of "Spontaneous" Metastases and Intravenously Injected Particles of VX₂ Carcinoma and Anatomy of Pulmonary Vessels

William H. Knisely and M. S. Mahaley, Jr.

Departments of Anatomy and Medicine, Duke University

The purpose of these experiments was to obtain information on the relationship between size and distribution of tumor metastases. Historically, there have been two supposedly contradictory explanations for the distributions of metastases. The earlier is that which has become associated with Paget(1). He dramatically stated the position that certain tissues were favorable for given tumors as certain soils were for given seeds. This hypothesis is still called the "fertile soil" theory(2). The other theory is one that Ewing stated in the first edition of his book(3), but left out of later editions, to the effect that all aspects of metastatic distribution would be explainable by the mechanisms of the circulation. This explanation is referred to as the "mechanical circulatory" theory.

There are two findings about metastasis which must be separately explained: the first is the *frequency distribution* of certain tumors in *given organs or tissues;* the second is the *differential rates of growth of given tumors in different tissues.* An explanation of the observed frequency distributions must include the following separable parts: (a) the *transport* of tumor particles *to* given locations, (b) the *arrest* of particles *at* given locations, and (c) the *survival* (and perhaps *growth*) at given locations. An explanation of the differential growth rates may include: (a) information on the ability for stomal formation, (b) available blood supply(s), and/or (c) any biochemical variations which are shown to be relevant.

The tumor which we used is the VX₂ rabbit squamous cell carcinoma. This tumor came about spontaneously in a viral-induced papilloma. Kidd and Rous reported on it in the late thirties and early forties(4). This tumor has been studied extensively in relation to the problem of metastasis(5, 6). Briefly, the kinds of things that have been done include studying the cell surface with electron microscopy(7); the cells are different from normal squamous cells. The rate of amoeboid motion is faster than normal squamous cells(8). It has been found that the adhesiveness of these cells is some 3 to 6 times less than that of normal squamous cells(9).

RHESUS MONKEY

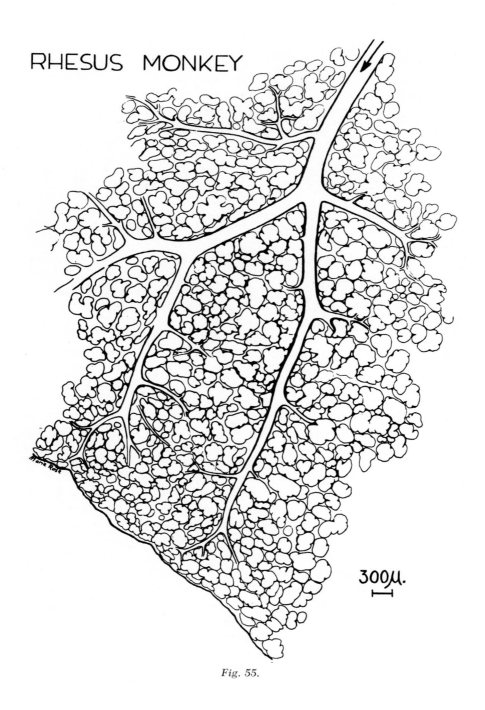

300μ.

Fig. 55.

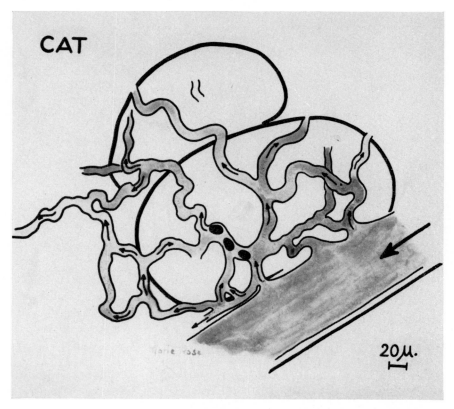

Fig. 56.

Dr. Williams studied the vascularization of this tissue in the rabbit ear chamber *in vivo*(10) and found that it did not become vascularized, as Dr. Algire(11) had shown to be the case in certain other tumors and as Williams had seen in a number of other tissues.

The work we carried out really followed work done by Zeidman and Buss at Pennsylvania(12). They took tumors grown in thigh muscle and sliced these up, ran them through a sieve, and then took the cell suspension which passed through the sieve and injected it intravenously into rabbits. Simultaneously, they cut the abdominal aorta and collected the aortic blood. They then injected this aortic blood into another group of rabbits, and produced tumors in several of the latter group. The authors concluded that transpulmonary passage had occurred. From our experiments we concur that small VX_2 tumor particles can pass through the lungs. The authors had made very small particles which passed through the lung and produced tumors; however, the VX_2 has been found in every

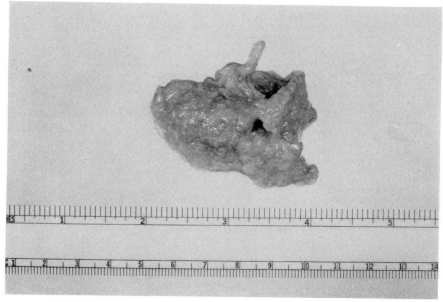

Fig. 57.

experimental situation always to metastasize to lung, but usually never beyond the lung.

There are several aspects of the anatomy of pulmonary vasculature which I want to show you (Fig. 55). Dr. Irwin has already shown you enough lung so that I can go through this very rapidly. What we did was to run the tumor particles through three sieves and ended up with particles which passed through a sieve with a 38-micron opening, which we called *small particles,* and which we hoped would end way out here peripherally, or perhaps within the capillaries, or perhaps pass through the lung. We also had a second size of particle with an approximate range of from 38 to 246 μ called *medium,* and a third size which we called *large,* which were from 246 to 495 μ.

We chose these three sizes because we hoped that some of the small ones would end up peripherally, and/or perhaps pass through as stated, and we hoped that some of the medium ones would not pass so far and produce tumors within this limited area of the terminal pulmonary vasculature which we could then study *in vivo.* The dimension where the arteries come up out of the alveoli has been reported by Dr. Irwin(13) to be about 150 μ in the larger vessels. Sometimes they are a little bigger than that. We hoped that the largest-sized particles would end up down deeper within the lung, and therefore in a definably different environment.

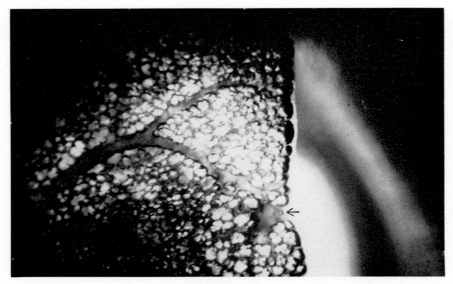

Fig. 58.

Fig. 56 will show you one alveolus, similar again to the high-power motion picture which Dr. Irwin showed. There are relatively capillary-sized vessels coming off laterally from a relatively large arteriole. This was made at 360X magnification, and it is blown up again, of course, in projection. We thought that, undoubtedly, if a tumor embolus stopped at "X," it might continue to "receive" blood. It might continue to be nourished; this would be a definably different environment from that of a much larger central embolus or a more peripheral one.

We very soon found that we could identify, on a double-blind basis, those animals which had been injected intramuscularly and which had "spontaneous" metastases to the lung, from animals with the three sizes of intravenously injected particles, merely by looking at the lungs (Fig. 57). The spontaneous metastases were distributed throughout the lung, while the intravenously injected particles tended to be more on the dependent side at the time of injection; these were anesthetized animals, and we put the particles in by catheter in the external jugular(14-19).

The small particles tended to end up on the periphery, the medium-sized ones a little deeper within the lung, and the large particles much deeper within the lung.

Fig. 58 shows a very gross picture of one lesion, which is quite different from the lung that was shown previously. This is one lesion from the large intravenous particles.

Fig. 59 shows discrete, individual lesions. These are tumors from small, intravenously injected particles, and as you see, they are right on the

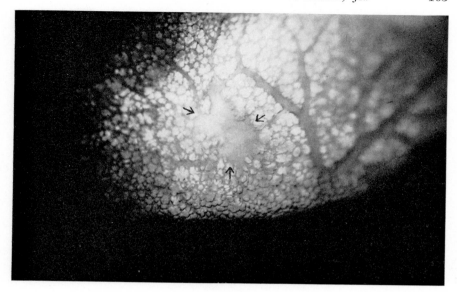

Fig. 59.

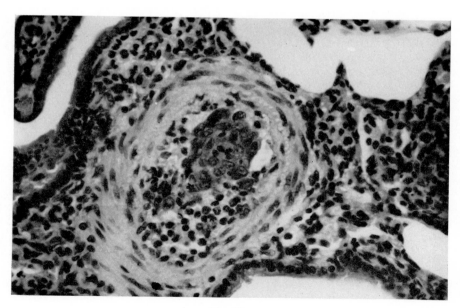

Fig. 60.

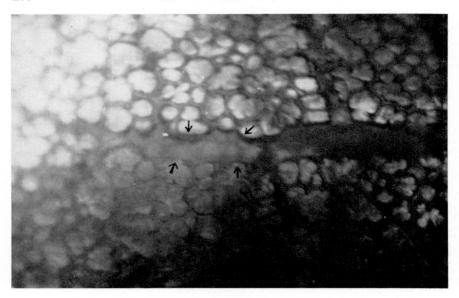

Fig. 61.

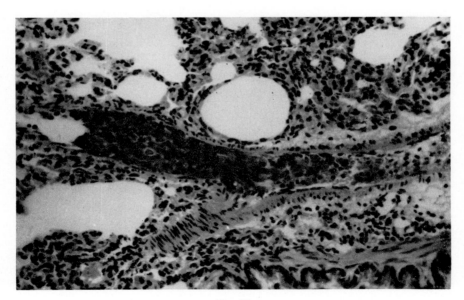

Fig. 62.

edge of the lung, in a region which cannot be occupied by anything much bigger than a capillary, or two or three times the size of a capillary.

Fig. 60 shows a section of a "spontaneous" metastasis within a pulmonary arteriole; one of the things we more or less stumbled across in this study was the fact that we have rather good information on the sizes of "spontaneous" metastases of this tumor. This is a cross-section of one small arteriole.

Fig. 61 is a view by *in vivo* methods and Fig. 62 is a view by section methods. These are tumors from spontaneous metastases from thigh-injected rabbits. We found that these metastases tended to localize in such small arterioles. However, these "spontaneous" metastases cannot be measured precisely because we do not know the exact time of arrival: thus they may have grown for some unknown length of time before they were measured. However, we found that the minimum size of the vast majority of these was from 100 to 175 μ. This is probably larger than has been thought, based on the studies of the easy dissociability of these cells mentioned above(9).

Fig. 63 shows an area of lung overlapping with the next one which will be shown. I want to show them both so that you can see the relatively normal vasculature in these positions—away from the tumor.

Fig. 64 shows a transplant from a medium-sized intravenously injected particle. Here I can pause and talk a little about the vascularization of the tumor itself. You can see a relatively normal pulmonary arteriole,

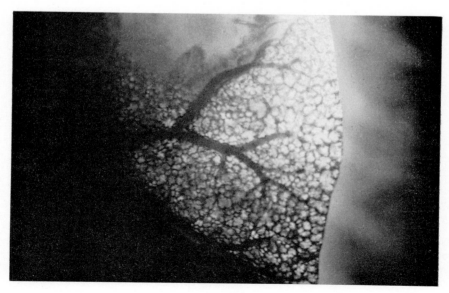

Fig. 63.

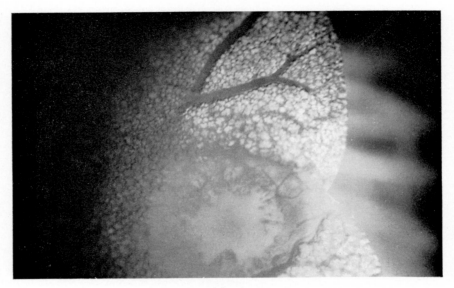

Fig. 64.

although, obviously, there is not normal vasculature on the side of the vessel toward the tumor. The lung is slightly "puckered in." Sometimes such lesions were adherent to the parietal pleura.

The tumor itself consisted of a growing edge, which surrounded a vascularized area of tissue with vessels pointing inward, which is certainly not a normal position of pulmonary vessels, and this vascularized area surrounded a non-vascular area with a necrotic center.

The problem which Dr. Williams reported on(10) was whether or not any vessels present in this tumor represented neovascularization. We certainly can't answer that, but it looks as if, in such a position as that, the vessels may be merely incorporated and rearranged pulmonary vessels. I am not sure that is true; however, they certainly do not have the anatomy of normal pulmonary vessels, and they are saccular and dilated and torn up, and therefore are not normal "systemic" vessels either.

Now, another point relative to circulation and relevant to the problem of metastatic distribution and growth rate can be mentioned here. The pulmonary tumors on the edge of the lung became necrotic when they were about 2.4 mm. in diameter. Those which were deep within the lung, produced by large intravenous particles, became necrotic when they were about one or two centimeters in diameter, and the growth rates likewise were considerably different for these two locations.

We found (Fig. 65) that the growth rate of the large particles deep within the lung was much more similar to the growth rates in liver and in thigh muscle. These curves were established by the measurement of four or five tumors selected at random in each series of animals from each category. They represent only pulmonary growths. This curve (solid line) represents spontaneous metastases, these (dotted line) are transplants from small, these (dot-dash line) from medium, and these (dash line) from large particles. We won't argue about any differences in the spon-

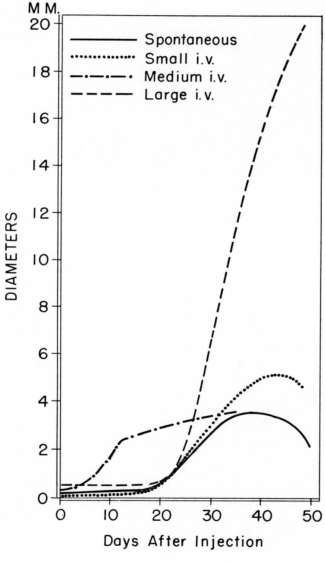

Fig. 65.

taneous, small, and medium groups. Certainly, however, the *rate* of growth and the *absolute size* attained by the large intravenously injected particles were different from the three others. The growth rate of intravenously injected particles within the lung resembled the growth rate of particles within the liver in animals injected intravenously with small particles much more closely than it did the rates of other intrapulmonary tumors. Hepatic tumors from intravenous injection of small particles grew much faster than did intrapulmonary tumors in the same animals, and it is assumed that these hepatic tumors resulted from the transpulmonary passage of such small particles. I don't know any way to guess that the hepatic tumors grew from particles which got there *sooner* than did those in the lung. Thus there is a difference in growth rate from organ to organ. We saw a difference, then, in growth rates within the lung, from one position to another, on one hand, and between the edge of the lung and the liver on the other.

Well, I think that we can now say the following about the problem of the classical argument about metastatic distribution: Within the lung there is a difference in the rate of growth from one location to another, and there is a difference from the lung to the liver. This certainly argues strongly in favor of the existence of a different biochemistry in one organ and another as affecting metastatic growth. However, it is obviously somewhat more complicated. The large particles deep within the lung may have had a bronchial arterial supply as well as a pulmonary arterial supply. Similarly, the growths within the liver may have had hepatic arterial supply as well as portal venous supply. However, the kidney tumors grew faster also than pulmonary growths near the edge.

The other classical argument about specific locations being more frequent sites of metastases was encountered as well. The liver was a much more frequent site of distribution than any organ other than the lung. It was the only extrapulmonary site in which tumor was found in the 50-some animals injected in the thigh muscle; three of these rabbits had hepatic lesions.

I think, based upon these findings, and upon what we have read in the literature, one specific point by Willis(2) must be criticized. This is a point which is fundamental in his own arguing about metastatic distribution, and, we think, is fundamental in terms of understanding the systemic distribution of small particles. Willis strongly favors the so-called "fertile soil" theory. He states this clearly in his 1952 edition of *The Spread of Tumors in the Human Body*. He came to this conclusion in a way, we think, because he does not believe in the transpulmonary passage of tumor particles, and, he came to that conclusion by what looks to us as a very illogical series of events.

He measured 100 human pulmonary emboli, which ran from 15 to

650 μ, and he concluded from this that these data represented the size range of tumor particles which had been in the venous blood. Obviously, if small particles had passed through the lung, he could not have measured them. The measured emboli, then, are not a valid criterion for the *smallest* aspect of the size range.

REFERENCES

1. Paget, S. The distribution of secondary growths in cancer of the breast. Lancet. *1*:571-73 (1889).
2. Willis, R. A. *The Spread of Tumors in the Human Body*. 2nd ed.; St. Louis, Mo.: The C. V. Mosby Co., 1952, p. 167.
3. Ewing, J. *Neoplastic Diseases*. 1st ed.; Philadelphia: W. B. Saunders Co., 1919, p. 86.
4. Kidd, J. G., and P. Rous. A transplantable rabbit carcinoma originating in a virus induced papilloma and containing the virus in masked or altered form. J. exp. Med. *71*:813-38 (1940).
5. Coman, D. R. Mechanisms responsible for the origin and distribution of blood-borne tumor metastases: A review. Cancer Res. *13*:397-404 (1953).
6. Zeidman, I. Metastasis: A review of recent advances. Cancer Res. *17*: 157-62 (1957).
7. Coman, D. R., and T. F. Anderson. A structural difference between the surfaces of normal and of carcinomatous epidermal cells. Cancer Res. *15*:541-43 (1955).
8. Enterline, H. T., and D. R. Coman. The amoeboid motility of human and animal neoplastic cells. Cancer. *3*:1033-38 (1950).
9. Coman, D. R. Decreased mutual adhesiveness, a property of cells from squamous cell carcinomas. Cancer Res. *4*:625-29 (1944).
10. Williams, R. G. The vascularity of normal and neoplastic grafts *in vivo*. Cancer Res. *11*:139-44 (1951).
11. Algire, G. H., and H. W. Chalkley. Vascular reactions of normal and malignant tissues *in vivo*. I. J. nat. Cancer Inst. *6*:73-85 (1945).
12. Zeidman, I., and J. M. Buss. Transpulmonary passage of tumor cell emboli. Cancer Res. *12*:731-33 (1952).
13. Irwin, J. W., W. S. Burrage, C. E. Aimar, and R. W. Chesnut, Jr. Microscopical observations of the pulmonary arterioles, capillaries, and venules of living guinea pigs and rabbits. Anat. Rec. *119*:391-408 (1954).
14. Abernathy, R. S., G. B. Smith, Jr., and D. T. Smith. The apical localization of reinfection pulmonary tuberculosis. II. Selective localization of experimental emboli. Amer. Rev. Tuberc. *70*:557-69 (1954).
15. Kretz, R. Uber die Lokalisation der Lungenembolism. Zbl. allg. Path. *21*:195-97 (1913).
16. Kretz, R. Zur Kenntnis der Gesetze der embolischen Verschleppung. Verb. dtsch. path. Ges. *15*:273-83 (1912).
17. Rupp, A. Zur Lokalisation der Lungenembolien. Arch. f. kl. ch. *115*: 689-90 (1921).
18. Georgi, W. Experimentelle Untersuchungen Zur Embolielokalisation in der Lunge. Beitr. path. Anat. *54*:401 (1912).
19. Hofmann, W. Ueber die Lokalization von Embolien in der Lunge beim Menschen. Beitr. path. Anat. *54*:622-25 (1952).

20. Batson, O. V. The function of the vertebral veins and their role in the spread of metastases. Ann. Surg. *112*:138-49 (1940).
21. Batson, O. V. The role of vertebral veins in metastatic processes. Ann. Internat. Med. *16*:38-45 (1942).
22. Knisely, W. H., M. A. Mahaley, Jr., and H. H. Jett. Approximation of "total vascular space" and its distribution in three sizes of blood vessels in rats by plastic casts. Circulation Res. *6*:20-25 (1958).
23. Knisely, W. H., W. M. Satterwhite, Jr., and J. M. Wallace. An attempt to demonstrate pulmonary arteriovenous anastomoses in rabbits, cats, and dogs and discussion of literature pertaining to such shunts. Circulation. *14*:960-61 (1956).
24. Prinzmetal, M., E. M. Ornitz, Jr., B. Simkins, and H. C. Bergman. Arteriovenous anastomoses in liver, spleen and lungs. Amer. J. Physiol. *152*:48-52 (1948).
25. Bostroem, B., and J. Piiper. Concerning arterio-venous anastomoses and blood shunting in the lung. (In German). Pflug. Archiv. *261*:165-71 (1955).

Discussion

CHAIRMAN FOWLER: This presentation is now open for general discussion. Do we have any questions?

DR. A. M. RAPPAPORT (University of Toronto): I would like to ask Dr. Knisely if the tumors seen in the liver were supplied by arterioles or by venules mainly.

DR. IRWIN: A tumor particle, I suppose, would be rather a rigid mass, or, maybe, it isn't. I should like to ask that. How big a one does he think would go through the pulmonary circulation?

DR. KNISELY: Dr. Rappaport, I don't know the answer to your question. However, using the method that Dr. Batson(20, 21) evolved for studying the venous supply to the spinal column, we have injected methyl methacrylate into the vasculature of the legs of an animal with thigh tumors. I think that one might do the same thing and, perhaps, determine the answer to your question regarding tumors in the liver. We are really working now on several sets of experiments attempting to find out what are the limiting factors on systemic distribution. That is one of the ways we are trying to approach that problem(22).

With respect to the size of the particle, I think that there are several things I should say. Before we started this work, we used about 150 rabbits, cats, and dogs, and tried to determine the size of the largest particle which might go through the lung(23) and, like everybody else, when you carry out experiments and they don't agree with the literature, you become critical of the literature.

I am going to make a "straw man" out of Dr. Prinzmetal(24). He injected beads intravenously and then took the livers out, found beads in them, and assumed that they had necessarily gone through the lung. We did the same experiments, and showed that we could tie off all the arterial and portal venous supply to the liver and still get beads into the liver by way of retrograde flow down the thoracic inferior vena cava. However, if we made a "one-way valve" out of the thoracic portion of the inferior vena cava by ligating it and drawing blood from the hepatic vein and injecting it into the right heart, we couldn't get any beads into the liver, even though the arterial and venous supplies remained intact.

I think that there are two very good papers relevant to the sizes of particles that can go through the lung. One is by Dr. Irwin(13). Your measurement of the largest visible communications between pulmonary arteries and pulmonary veins is about 20 μ, and there is a paper in German with a series of very narrowly graded beads, by Bostroem and Piiper(25), in which they found, I believe, that they could get no particles 24 μ through, none of 22 μ, but a few of 19 μ. Then many particles would go through from 17 to 15 μ.

My own feeling is that the largest channels in healthy lungs are about 20 μ. Then I would add a word. I think that one must understand, in terms of metastatic distribution in the human, that in all probability the size of the particles which are released intravenously is the primary determinant of their distribution. The second determinant is the precise size of the vascular channel that a given particle enters. Whether or not a particle passes through the lung is determined by the size of the smallest particles present and the largest pulmonary vessels. The question we would like to get at in this argument is why particles are arrested in certain sites systemically. I think that there may be a "selective arrest" systemically of the smallest particles which pass through the lung, let's say from 15 to 20 μ in size. In this case, very minor absolute differences in the systemic dimensions might be critical differences.

DR. MELVIN KNISELY: Just one second. Gross anatomy is an obsolete subject, as we all know, but Patten showed that there was about a 25 to 33 per cent patent foramen ovale in the human specimens.

CHAIRMAN FOWLER: We are to have one more paper before the seventh inning, which will be by Dr. Silvio Baez of the Department of Anesthesiology, New York University–Bellevue Medical Center, on "Microcirculation in the Intramural Vessels of the Small Intestine in the Rat."

Microcirculation in the Intramural Vessels of the Small Intestine in the Rat

Silvio Baez

Department of Anesthesiology, New York University–Bellevue Medical Center

The precise vascular connections between the large distributing arteries and collecting veins of the intestine and their functional regulation have not been well documented and are largely a matter of inference and varied opinion. Most of the available information about the anatomical organization of this vascular bed is based on studies of fixed, stained, or injected material. Data dealing with its functional activity, although more quantitative are admittedly fragmentary and based on (1) studies of thermal changes recorded in localized tissue layers, or on (2) over-all circulatory measurements limited to the larger blood vessels of the intestine. There is a need for co-ordinated studies of the morphology and dynamics of the blood vessels of the organ, made under carefully controlled conditions.

Much of our basic knowledge of the structure and function of the microcirculation derives from the studies utilizing direct microscopy of living material developed by, among others, A. Krogh, E. R. Clark, R. E. Chambers, B. W. Zweifach, M. Knisely, P. A. Nicoll, B. R. Lutz, G. P. Fulton. The validity and unique contribution of this type of experimental approach are generally accepted. Although almost every accessible tissue and appendage has been extensively examined, the intestine has not been subjected to such study, probably because of technical difficulties related to obtaining adequate optical conditions.

This preliminary presentation will be concerned with microcirculatory studies in the rat ileum. It was undertaken in the belief that information provided by this method of approach would add necessary depth and perspective to our present picture of structure and function of the vessels in the alimentary canal.

This study, initiated in the Department of Medicine, Cornell Medical Center, and continued in the Department of Anesthesiology, New York University–Bellevue Medical Center, was aided in part by grants from the Josiah Macy, Jr. Foundation and from the United States Public Health Service, Grant H-2743. The skilled assistance of Jack Godrich and Sarah Gray in carrying out these studies is gratefully acknowledged.

METHOD

A technique developed in our laboratory for trapping air or water within the intestinal lumen of the intact animal at physiological ranges of pressure allows effective transillumination at the desired plane of the tissue. An intestinal loop, so prepared, is exposed over a suitably shaped lucite frame, which replaces the microscope stage. The preparation is irrigated with gelatin-Ringer solution and the temperature controlled automatically by thermistor probes via a recording telethermometer. Physiological integrity of the vascular components of the tissue can be maintained intact for several hours, as determined by their reactivity to selected vasoactive drugs, according to previously reported criteria(3).

This technical approach affords a high degree of optical resolution and is quite versatile experimentally, since except for the small loop of exposed bowel, the animal is intact and suitable for exposure to various experimental modalities and measurements. Briefly, at low power of the microscope, and by carefully propping the organ with cotton wads, the number and distribution of the large supplying arteries and accompanying veins of both anterior and posterior wall can be determined, as well as their relation to the small vasa recta. Also, the type of vascular connections at the antimesenteric border of the organ can readily be established in the same exposed segment. At higher magnification and with water immersion lens, the vascular components of the submucous plexus and dependent vessels destined to the muscular coat can be clearly traced to their final ramifications. Arteries to the mucosal layer can be followed up to their penetration of the base of the villi. Except for the villi then, the microcirculation of the entire mural vasculature of the intestine can be brought under direct scrutiny by the presently proposed technique. The microcirculation of the villi, not included in this presentation, is under current study in our laboratory, using a different technical approach, and the results of the study will be published elsewhere.

In addition to determining the anatomical organization of this vascular bed, the preparation permits analysis of important basic features of vascular behavior which participate in the local regulation of blood flow: (a) micrometric measurements can be made under basal conditions of representative vessels supplying each layer of the wall; (b) the presence of spontaneous vasomotion can be determined in the small muscular components of the bed, and slow-caliber changes of the larger supplying vessels, occurring spontaneously or induced by vasotropic drugs, can be readily measured and recorded by cinemicrophotography; (c) the influence of neurogenic factors on intestinal vascular tone and spontaneous motion can be studied by electrical stimulation of the splanchnic nerve and its peripheral branches, as well as in denervated preparations.

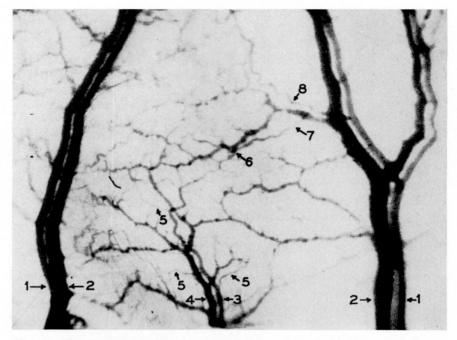

Fig. 66. Photomicrograph from mesentery border of rat ileum (from Kodachrome transparency). (1) Main incoming arteries with (2) accompanying veins (large vasa recta). Small vasa recta, artery (3), and vein (4). Mucosal arteries (5) originating from main trunk (6). End portion of small vasa recta inosculates with a secondary submucous arterial loop (7), which in turn arises from a main arterial arcade (8) in the submucosa. (7 ×)

DESCRIPTION OF SUBMUCOUS PLEXUS

The two types of vasa recta, described in various mammals and man by Eiseberg(4), Noer(5), and Jacobson and Noer(6), among others, were also found to occur in the small intestine of the rat. The main arteries, typical diameter size from 60 to 80 μ, pierce the muscularis in the mesenteric region of the organ at regular intervals of 4 to 6 mm. After a variable length as a single trunk, in the submucosa these vessels divide into two or three branches. Each in turn breaks up into four to six smaller (30 to 40 μ) branches, and reaching the antimesenteric border, anastomoses with similar arterial branches from the opposite side. These antimesenteric vessels, together with those given off by the main trunk (3 to 5, Fig. 66) at various degrees of angularity inosculate with similar branches from neighboring vasa recta to form the main system of mural anastomotic arteries in the submucosa.

Although differing in general direction, the former transversal, the latter more or less parallel to the longitudinal axis of the organ, the vascular components of the main arterial arcade share enough in anatomical, architectural, and physiological characteristics to warrant grouping into one category: (a) averaging from 30 to 40 μ in diameter in the resting state, they are all located in the same outermost plane of the submucosa; (b) all originate secondary arcades or loops, mucosal arteries, and vessels to nourish the muscular coat; (c) they equally exhibit, with the periodic change in vasomotor tone of their component vessels, a constant change in direction of blood flow within the lumen. No special arrangements, such as the "Indian club" formation described by Nicoll and Webb(7) in the arcuate arteriolar system of the bat wing, were seen at the origin of these or other arteries in the intestinal wall in the rat.

Small vasa recta, typical diameter size from 30 to 40 μ, also arising from the last mesenteric arcade, reach the gut wall, there to interspace between the large ones. The majority of these vessels scarcely reach a third of the width of the organ (3, Fig. 66) and terminate by anastomosing with secondary branches of the lower arcades. They chiefly give vessels to the submucosa and muscular coats in the neighborhood of the mesenteric border and, in general, are reminiscent of those arteries described by Barlow(8) for the lesser curvature of the stomach. Eiseberg(4) found them to be rare in the duodenum and more numerous in the jejunum and ileum, as was confirmed in our laboratory. Our direct count, from pylorous to caecum in a number of rats of various age groups, gave an average ratio of 1 to 2 of small vasa recta to large arteries.

This meshwork of interconnected arterial vessels with its secondary and tertiary loops in the submucosa (Fig. 67), located as a crossroad between the inner absorptive surface of the gastrointestinal tract and its outer motor smooth-muscle coat, supplies sets of vessels to those layers, which are very different architecturally at their final destination. Perhaps because of its strategic location, in a more direct line of cardiac and neuromotor influences than its dependent plexus of the mucosal and muscular coats, it exhibits a unique hemodynamic feature hitherto undescribed. Blood flow, which is continuous as far as the main supplying arteries (large and small vasa recta) and undirectional toward the periphery, is altered upon reaching the submucous arterial plexus. In any given main arterial arcade, blood may be supplied at one moment exclusively by one of the parent arteries. At the next moment, however, flow begins from the opposite side, thus completely reversing its direction. Or, more often, the arcade exhibits an oppositely oriented flow, which reaches a point of temporary equilibrium at any point along its length, usually at the origin of a mucosal artery, which at this moment thus receives blood from both sides. The balance is broken, however, with the subsequent change in territorial supply by one or the other of the arterial components. This pattern of blood flow is to be expected in any system of interconnected arterial vessels. It results from alternating changes in vasomotor tone of the component vessels of the arcade and assures adequate, continuous flow of blood to dependent mucosal and muscular coat vessels. The site of flow equilibration is easily recognized as a clear zone in a segment of the arcade from 80 to 150 μ in length. This zone results from a "microturbulence" created by the blood rushing from opposite directions, which momentarily relegates red cells and leucocytes a little upstream on both sides of the converging currents, thus leaving only clear plasma and a few platelets. When this occurs at the point of origin of a mucosal vessel, plasma is preferentially "skimmed" into it.

This reversal of flow, with its resulting sites of equilibrium and plasma skimming, has not been seen beyond the secondary arterial loops in the plexus. Its implications for local circulatory homeostasis require further study.

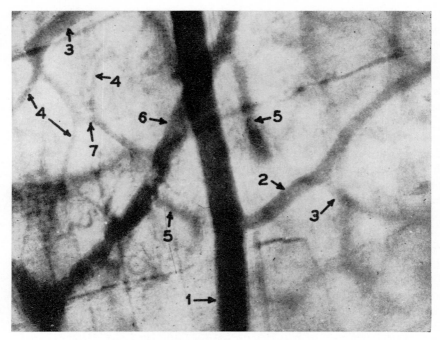

Fig. 67. Photomicrograph from anterior wall of ileum (from Kodachrome transparency). (1) Main submucous anastomotic artery. (2) Secondary arterial loop, giving off (3) a mucosal artery. In left upper corner (3), a terminal segment of a mucosal artery breaks up into branches (4) to neighboring villi. (5) Emerging mucosal venules join submucous venules (6). A final interarterial anastomosis can be seen (7) deep in submucosa. (275 ×)

MUSCULAR COAT

Vessels destined to nourish the muscular coat arise from the proximal end of mucosal arteries or from secondary arcades in the submucosa. The majority are metarterioles, averaging from 18 to 24 μ in diameter. Turning upward, they reach the plane of cleavage between the circular and longitudinal muscles and run, in this plane, in a general direction transverse to the long axis of the organ. No branches are given off by

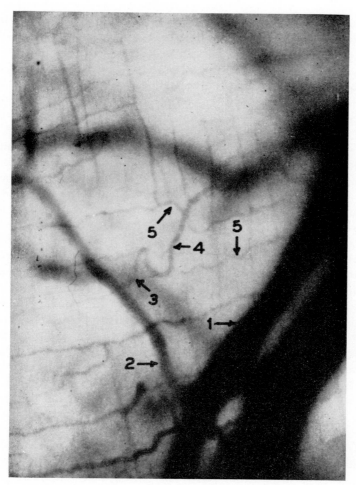

Fig. 68. Photomicrograph from anterior wall of ileum (from Kodachrome transparency). (1) Main arterial and venous limbs of submucous plexus. (2) Main anastomosing arterial branch. (3) Mucosal artery, which disappears from focus after giving off an arteriole (4) to muscular layer. (5) Metarterioles supplying capillaries for oppositely oriented muscle bundles. (92 $\times$)

these vessels until they reach the intermuscular septum. There two sets of capillary vessels arise at regular intervals: (a) those destined for the circular muscle bundles remain on the same plane as the parent vessels; (b) those for the longitudinal bundles, however, twist further outward. These small vessels, some with precapillary sphincters, others without, run parallel to one another at 40- to 60-μ intervals, presumably to the muscle bundle (Fig. 68). They communicate freely with each other in the same plane, and with similar capillary vessels of the adjacent layer of the muscle. Thus they form a sort of double-decked meshwork of interconnecting capillary plexus. The parent vessel, after variable lengths of 0.5 to 1 mm., may divide in two or, without dividing, may arch inward upon itself and become a venule. This, enlarged by other venules formed by neighboring capillaries, finds its way to a submucous vein. Thus the parent vessel, which arose singly in the submucosa, returns to the submucosa as a venule after giving out its capillary network, constituting a distinctly organized terminal vascular unit of the smooth muscle coat of the intestine.

The vascular bed of this layer, of capillary dimensions, is composed of both muscular and non-muscular elements. The muscular components are the centrally located metarterioles with their muscular precapillary offshoots, which serve as an efficient controlling mechanism for blood flow throughout the myriads of dependent, non-muscular capillaries. The precapillaries not only exhibit the phenomenon of active "vasomotion," as described by Chambers and Zweifach(9) and Nicoll and Webb(10), but with the parent metarteriole, they constitute the most highly reactive elements thus far studied in the entire mural vasculature. This is readily demonstrated by the action of chemical vasoconstrictor and vasodilator drugs, as well as by the effect of controlled gradients of applied intraluminal pressure. The endothelial capillary bed, organized around this centrally located, highly responsive muscular component, exhibits a pattern of blood flow which is to great extent independent of hemodynamic events in the underlying submucous plexus and mucosal layer. Periodic ebb and flow of blood through the capillary bed of the muscular coat occurs independently of sudden changes in the direction of flow in the submucous arterial plexus. Also, during hemorrhagic hypotension the entire vasculature of the muscular coat may be excluded from the circulation, while the submucous arterial plexus and its dependent mucosal arteries still exhibit continuous blood flow.

Variations of this picture exist. The parent vessel may emerge as a short arteriole, from 28 to 35 μ in diameter (4, Fig. 69), which gives off two or three metarterioles only upon reaching the muscularis. Subsequently, however, the architectural arrangement conforms to the above description. The main trunk either turns inward to become a draining

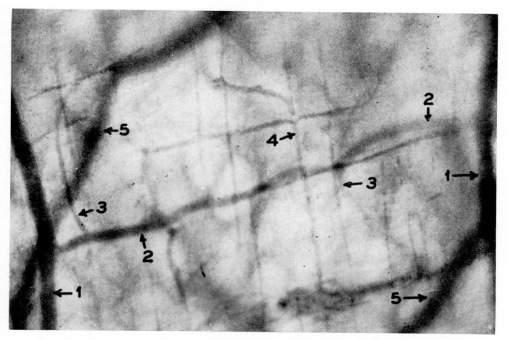

Fig. 69. Photomicrograph from antimesenteric border of ileum (from Kodachrome transparency). (1) Main submucous arteries. (2) Secondary connecting loop. (3) Mucosal arteries. (4) Terminal segment of metarteriole and capillary meshwork to circular muscle bundles. (5) Large submucous venules. In background, out of focus, are outlined bases of villi. (115 ×)

venule, thus forming a thoroughfare channel, or breaks up into two or three capillaries. Another important variation is found in the neighborhood of the mesenteric border. There the thoroughfare channel *per se,* or a vessel resulting from the aggregate of two or three capillaries, conveys blood directly to the vein accompanying the small vasa recta, thus avoiding the submucous plexus.

MUCOSAL ARTERIES

The mucosal artery has been observed from its point of departure from the main arterial arcade or secondary loops to its entry at the base of the villi. After supplying a vessel to the muscular coat, as described above, it continues toward the muscularis mucosa, giving off in its course one or two short vessels, which immediately break up into three to six capillaries. These, after a brief semicircular turn, reunite as a venule to join a small submucous vein. The capillary vessels thus arranged in the submucosa surround an area of tissue, from 40 to 60 μ in diameter, which perhaps is occupied by lymphatic channels or nerve cell aggregates.

These vascular formations seem to correspond to those described by Moll as "rete"(11). They communicate freely with each other and with similar neighboring formations. Deeper in the submucosa all mucosal arteries, after sending a short anastomotic vessel to similar mucosal arteries, give off one or two more vessels. Capillary vessels from the latter again arrange themselves in a semicircular manner. Now, however, the area of tissue surrounded is larger, 80 to 100 μ in diameter, regularly distributed throughout the field, and clearly seen to correspond to gland tissue and bases of the villi. The end segment of the main vessel usually joins a venule, which drains two or three villi. The terminal portion of the mucosal artery, now reduced in size by half, penetrates the base of the villi as a single- or double-branched vessel.

Again exception must be made concerning some mucosal arteries supplying the mesenteric border of the organ. Here many of these vessels arise directly from the small vasa recta.

The mucosal artery, from its origin to its entry into the villi, appears to be invested with contractile muscular elements, as judged by the intermittent ebb and flow of blood still seen in the deepest vascular organization at the base of the villi, which must result from the activity of muscular precapillary sphincters. Although the mucosal artery exhibits a rapid and continuous flow of blood, periodic alterations supervene: (a) the amount of blood flow may decrease momentarily due to slight changes in lumen diameter brought about by phasic changes in the tonus of the smooth muscle cells surrounding the vessel; (b) the quality of the blood may be altered when plasma is "skimmed" into the vessels, as previously described.

ARTERIOVENOUS ANASTOMOSIS

Although it has been held that "in an organ of phasic function in nature, arteriovenous anastomosis is to be expected"(8), no such anastomosis has been observed in our studies. The submucous plexus of interconnecting arteries and arterioles, of diameter size 28 to 60 μ, although intricate, can be perfectly followed under the microscope to its finest ramifications. In no instance, in separated zones of jejunum and ileum examined, have we found a short cut of blood from arterial to venous plexus. The only sites where blood of arterial color has been seen to divert into a vein are (a) in the mesenteric border, through the thoroughfare channels leading from muscular arterioles to the venule accompanying the small vasa recta, and (b) at the base of the villi, as described above.

VENULES AND VEINS

Two or three venules arising from neighboring villi converge to form

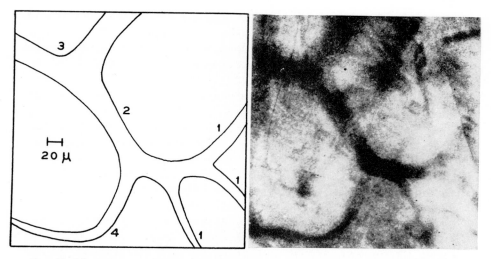

Fig. 70. Photomicrograph and projection drawing of base of villi (from Kodachrome transparency). (1) Converging venules from neighboring villi. (2) Mucosal venule on its way to join a submucosal venule (3). A vessel of capillary dimensions (4) which injects arterial blood into mucosal venule. (275 ×)

a slightly larger mucosal venule (2, Fig. 70). This, after receiving an arterial vessel of capillary dimensions from a branch of the nearest mucosal arteriole, runs a short distance, 100 to 150 μ, to join other similarly organized mucosal venules. The resultant small vein, arching outward, emerges into the submucosa. There it joins with other neighboring veins to form an intricate anastomosing venous arcade. All along the course to the large draining veins, these submucous arcades are enlarged by venules proceeding from the outer muscular coat.

Discrete smooth muscle cells appear in the wall of the small collecting veins in the submucosa and become more prominent in the larger components of the arcade. Slow changes in lumen diameter exhibited by these large veins from time to time, as well as the beaded appearance of the small tributaries in the submucous venous plexus, are effected by these contractile elements in the wall.

Drainage through the muscular coat and mucosal venules is rapid and unidirectional. In the submucosal venous plexus, however, backflow occurs.

SUMMARY

1. A technique for microcirculatory studies of the intestinal vasculature in the intact small laboratory animal has been developed.

2. The organization of the submucous arterial plexus and the struc-

tural makeup of the dependent plexus of the smooth muscle coat and most of the mucosal layer is described.

3. Some of the constant basic characteristics of flow pattern in the meshwork of interconnected large submucous arteries have been established:

(a) it serves as an efficient pool of blood to dependent inner and outer plexuses;

(b) imbalance in vasomotor tone adjustments in component vessels of an arcade create "microturbulence," which results in periodic changes in quality of blood flowing into mucosal arteries.

4. The capillary bed in the muscular coat layer constitutes a double-decked meshwork of interconnected endothelial vessels, arising from metarterioles which run in the cleavage plane of connective tissue between the inner circular and outer longitudinal muscle bundles, and terminating as preferential channels or abruptly into three or four capillaries. Intermittent circulation through the bed is regulated by the periodic vasomotion of the parent metarteriole and precapillary sphincters.

5. Mucosal arterioles exhibit continuous blood circulation. Dependent vascular twigs in the submucosa and at the base of the villi, however, show an intermittent flow.

6. A variation in vascular organization is described in the antimesenteric border of the intestine, due to the presence of interspersed small vasa recta. Blood return from the muscular coat in this region is effected, not through the submucous venous plexus, as in the rest of the organ, but through the vein accompanying the small vasa recta.

7. There is no true arteriovenous anastomosis between the large arteries and veins of the submucous plexus nor between the arterioles and venules of the muscular coat. Only at the base of the villi does there exist a shunt of arterial blood to mucosal venules.

REFERENCES

1. Grayson, J. The measurement of intestinal blood flow in man. J. Physiol. *114*:419-34 (1951).
2. Selkurt, E. E., M. P. Scibetta, and T. E. Cull. Hemodynamics of intestinal circulation. Circulation Res. *6*:92-99 (1958).
3. Zweifach, B. W. "Microscopic observations of circulation in rat mesoappendix and dog omentum: Use in study of vasotropic substances" in *Methods in Medical Research,* ed. V. R. Potter. Chicago: The Year Book Publishers, Inc., 1951.
4. Eiseberg, H. B. Intestinal arteries. Anat. Rec. *28*:227-42 (1924).
5. Noer, R. J. The blood vessels of the jejunum and ileum: A comparative study of man and certain laboratory animals. Amer. J. Anat. *73*:293-334 (1943).

6. Jacobson, L. F., and R. J. Noer. The vascular pattern of the intestinal villi in various laboratory animals and man. Anat. Rec. *114*:85-101 (1952).
7. Nicoll, P. A., and R. L. Webb. "Vascular patterns and active vasomotion as determiners of flow through minute vessels" in *Trans. Second Conf. on Microcirculatory Physiol. and Pathol.* Baltimore: The Williams & Wilkins Co., 1955, pp. 291-308.
8. Barlow, J. E. "Vascular patterns in the alimentary canal" in CIBA Foundation Symposium Publication, *Visceral Circulation*, ed. G. E. Wolstenholme. London: J. & A. Churchill, Ltd., 1953, pp. 21-36.
9. Chambers, R., and B. W. Zweifach. Topography and function of the mesentery capillary circulation. Amer. J. Anat. *75*:173-205 (1944).
10. Nicoll, P. A., and R. L. Webb. Blood circulation in the subcutaneous tissue of the living bat's wing. New York Acad. Sc. *47*:697-711 (1946).
11. Moll, F. P. Die Blut- und Lymphwege im Dünndarm des Hundes. Abh. sächs. Ges. (akad.) Wiss. *14*:151-88 (1887).
12. Muratori, G. Contributo alla vascolarizzazione sanguigna del linfo-noduli intestinali dell' uomo. Att. Ist. veneto. *2*:479 (1941).
13. Spanner, R. Neue Befunde über die Blutwege der Darmwand und ihre funktionele Bedeutung. Morph. Jb. *69*:394-454 (1932).

DISCUSSION

CHAIRMAN FOWLER: This presentation is now open for discussion generally.

DR. MARY P. WIEDEMAN (Temple University School of Medicine): Dr. Baez, did you ever see any active vasomotion in the veins? You mentioned it in the terminal arterioles.

DR. IRWIN: You used three words, and I would like to know how you differentiated those three vessels. You said, "metarteriole, arteriole capillary, and venous capillary." What was your basis for differentiating those three vessels?

DR. MELVIN KNISELY: I would like to set up a quick background for the importance of these venous anastomoses and whether or not they exist. One concept in the literature is that the portal vein bed is a reservoir with, perhaps, moving blood, and blood moving at various rates but with varying capacity. I think it was Mall, in about 1890, who showed connections across the roots of the villi, whereby arterial blood can go into veins. I think that there is one connection on each villus, or perhaps two. I have forgotten the species, but it was probably the dog and cat.

Rudolph Spanner has been publishing periodically on arterial anastomoses in the gastrointestinal tract. This whole idea is extremely important. It must be a mechanism which can fill the portal reservoir very rapidly and, of course, it would run arterial blood into the stems or the roots of the portal vein. We are not used to thinking about that.

If I understood correctly, I think that Dr. Baez said that he saw arteries with a diameter of about 18 to 20 μ, going across the roots of the villi, or something like that. That is a tremendously important set of problems, in which there may well be differences from species to species, too.

DR. ZWEIFACH: It is becoming increasingly apparent that the complexity of the vascular architecture in the gut makes it necessary to rely on several criteria to establish the presence or absence of arteriovenous anastomoses. Many of the older concepts—including those of Spanner— are based in large part upon examination of fixed sections. It is extraordinarily difficult, with this vast network of venules, interarcading venules, and interarcading arterioles, to establish paths of blood flow by this means. One can be easily led astray. Even in the stomach, where Barlow has described numerous anastomoses, there is no functional evidence to corroborate this interpretation. Actually, there is no good evidence for the presence of arteriovenous anastomoses in the gastrointestinal tract, with the exception of the small arterial vessels, which, at the base of the villus, connect directly with some of the venules. These vessels are not, however, the structures referred to in the literature. Previous workers have referred to extensive connections between arteries and veins. Such shunts cannot be seen in hemorrhage, even after the blood flow through the bowel has been extensively curtailed.

It would appear that the whole question of arteriovenous anastomoses could be profitably reinvestigated, using a double technique; that is, an examination of living material, and then injecting or fixing the material and restudying the same site.

CHAIRMAN FOWLER: Along these lines, I think that double observation is required in all this work. I think, one way or another, we ought to have confirmation or disagreement using fixed material. It is not too hard to fix most material used for small blood vessel work and then study it in stained preparations.

DR. CHESTER HYMAN (University of Southern California School of Medicine): I would like to extend your plea for a double approach. I would prefer a triple approach. It seems to me that the morphological demonstration of vessels of a given caliber, or vessels with a given relationship to their parent vessel, reaching from the arterial to the venous side, does not tell the entire story. What the physiologist is interested in is whether or not there are ways for the blood to reach the venous side without coming into equilibrium with the fluids of the tissue that it is passing through. And so a third set of techniques based on the physiologic determination of shunt flow is, I think, essential in many of these problems.

DR. MELVIN KNISELY: Just trying to summarize, I think that in several different places if you look at Spanner's pictures with reference to some of his literature, you will, of course, find some of the things, but not always.

When you study the dead, you are always stuck with the problem of whether the stuff was overdistended in setting it up, and, although I hate to confess it, when you are studying the living, you do not necessarily know how widely these things did dilate by seeing the diameter they have at any one time. In general, we like to study anatomy first and then, after a while, maybe, fiddle with pharmacology.

The chap at Marquette University, the small collecting channel man, Desach, wrote a paper on the technique for studying liver that you should read. He was a physiologist, pretty thoroughly educated on the use of drugs, and he did experiments which nobody in his right mind would do at all. He subjected the living organs to pharmacologically massive doses of various drugs, and then he froze the tissue or fixed it by the Spalteholz technique, which gives this transparent stuff, suspended in vinegar and oil. Then, if you are in your right mind, you cut thin sections and look at them. But he wasn't. He cut sections 200 or 300 μ thick and looked at them with low-power electron microscopy. He examined them histologically by ultraviolet, and found wonderful sections of all kinds. I don't think that you would find the maximum you can get in the liver until you really push them some way or other, and then, of course, take an awful beating in the next argument. But, to know the ultimate physiology, you have to know the degree of dilatation, correlated with filling and emptying the reservoir.

DR. BAEZ: Dr. Wiedeman, neither the submucous nor the muscular coat venules or veins have been observed to exhibit the phenomenon of active "vasomotion." The muscular venules and veins, however, are by no means inert vessels. They often show zones of contraction, alternating with zones of dilation or lack of contraction, thus appearing varicose. This motion, however, unrelated to mural contraction, is very slow in nature and not at all comparable to the rapid intermittent opening and closing of the muscular metarterioles and precapillaries.

In describing the organization of the minute vessels of the intestinal wall, Dr. Irwin, I have used the following terms: "metarteriole," "precapillary," and "endothelial capillary." "Metarteriole," beyond the arteriole, designates vessels of capillary dimensions, typical diameter size 18 to 24 μ, which in contrast to the parent arteriole present a discontinuous, smooth muscle investment along the wall. These give off "endothelial capillaries," some of which are endowed with a discrete number of smooth muscle cells at their origin, termed "precapillary" or "precapillary sphincter." The metarterioles and precapillaries are the only vascular elements in the terminal vascular bed which exhibit the rapidly occurring, intermittent spontaneous contraction and dilation termed "vaso-motion"(9). Now alteration of this intrinsic vascular phenomenon, by the influence of vasoactive drugs, moderate hemorrhage, and controlled gradients of intraluminal pressure, serves as a further basis to differentiate one vascular component from another.

The terms "arterial capillary" and "venous capillary," freely employed in the literature, are justified by the appearance of the vessels connecting the metarterioles and corresponding collecting venules, for all these capillary vessels, with or without precapillary sphincter, carry red arterial blood in the initial portion (arterial capillary) and become darker (venous capillary) as they approach the collecting vein. Here, however, I have used the term "arterial capillary" to designate the specific small vessel which, starting from the mucosal arteriole, reaches the mucosal venule and directly injects arterial blood into it.

I should like to comment on Dr. Knisely's remarks regarding arterio-venous anastomosis. In the ileum of the species studied, we are still searching unsuccessfully for a vessel which, bypassing the capillary bed, shunts blood directly from artery to vein. It definitely has not been seen to occur between arterial and venous components of the submucous arcades, of 30 to 80 μ in diameter, even under the effect of vasodilator drugs. Also, the small vessels, 18 to 20 μ in diameter, which have been seen to bring arterial blood to the venule draining the villi, are not true arteriovenous anastomoses, since in their course they give off a few branches to the neighboring structures (base of the villi, glands, etc.). Even these do not occur at every villus, because the arterial vessel reaches the venule which drains two or three villi (Fig. 70). In location, these vessels correspond to those described by Muratori(12) and Spanner(13) as arteriovenous anastomoses. If the capillary branches are excluded by spontaneous sphincteric action, these arterial vessels do then divert blood directly from the mucosal artery to the venules. Such exclusion of these capillary offshoots may well occur in injected and fixed preparation and would give the appearance of a true arteriovenous anastomosis.

CHAIRMAN FOWLER: The next paper is "A Study of Lymphatic Permeability to Albumin," to be given by Dr. Mayerson of Tulane University.

A Study of Lymphatic Permeability to Albumin

H. S. Mayerson

Department of Physiology, Tulane University School of Medicine

The experiments I am about to describe to you were performed by one of our medical students, Mr. Rodney M. Patterson. My colleague, Dr. Wasserman, and I are partners in the enterprise only to the extent that we furnished help and guidance when it was needed.

For a number of years, my colleagues and I have been concerned with the permeability of blood capillaries to macromolecules. We have shown that albumins, globulins, and dextrans of various molecular weights leak from blood capillaries, pass into the lymphatic system, and are returned to the circulation via the lymphatic ducts(1, 2). Quite naturally, we began to concern ourselves with the permeability of lymph ducts to these macromolecules. Does the capillary filtrate, once it is in the lymph ducts, empty without loss into the venous circulation, or is protein free to pass in and out of the lymphatic vessels throughout their lengths? Does any protein pass into the blood capillaries as the lymph traverses the lymph nodes and is in intimate contact with blood capillaries, or is any considerable amount of protein phagocytized by the reticulo-endo-thelial cells of the lymph nodes? Furthermore, to what degree, if any, is lymph shunted to the blood stream through lymph-blood vascular anastomoses other than the thoracic duct? Anomalous shunts, consisting of multiple outlets of the right and left ducts, have been described(3) as well as shunts between the right and left thoracic ducts in about 15 per cent of dogs(4).

Since we could not find these answers in the literature, we suggested to Mr. Patterson that he attempt to obtain some answers by injecting a known amount of albumin, labeled with radioactive iodine (I^{131}), into a leg lymphatic duct and see how much of the albumin he could recover in thoracic duct lymph and how much entered the circulation.

We used dogs anesthetized intravenously with a mixture of 150 mg. sodium barbital and 15 mg. nembutal per kilogram of body weight. Experience indicated the desirability of selecting large (15 kgs. or over),

This study was supported by a grant from the Medical Research and Development Division, Office of the Surgeon General, Department of the Army, under Contract DA-49-007-MD-39. Mr. Patterson was a Louisiana Heart Association Student Fellow during the summer of 1957.

129

long-legged, young animals, since these animals usually have large lymphatics, relatively unbranched and free of closely spaced valves. The details of the cannulation will be available elsewhere(5). Suffice to say that, with patience and fine technique, the lymphatic can be cannulated with polyethylene tubing and infusions given via this route.

The infusion fluid was made by mixing 1 to 3 ml. of stock iodinated albumin (prepared by incubating human serum albumin with radioactive iodine followed by dialysis to remove any free iodine) with 10 ml. of 25 per cent non-radioactive human serum albumin and diluting to 50 ml. with 0.9 per cent saline. Twenty-five ml. were infused at a constant rate of 0.5 ml. per minute for 50 minutes, and serial collections of thoracic duct lymph were made at 5-minute intervals starting at the beginning of the infusion. The albumin infusion was followed by an infusion of 50 ml. of 0.9 per cent saline at the same rate. Thus, the total infusion volume was 75 ml. given over a 150-minute period and allowing for 30 lymph samples during the experiments. Blood samples were obtained through the indwelling needle in a femoral artery at 30-minute intervals.

The protein in the plasma, lymph, and aliquots of the infusion fluid was precipitated with 20 per cent trichloro-acetic acid, centrifuged, and the supernatant analyzed to determine the amount of I^{131} which was not protein-bound. The protein-bound I^{131} was determined by subtracting free from total radioactivity. The total plasma volume was estimated as 5 per cent of the body weight and this value used in calculating total radioactivity in the circulation.

Edema fluid accumulated locally and to varying degrees at the infusion site in all experiments. It appeared to be minimized by direct lymphatic infusion of dibenzyline (10 to 20 cc. of 5 ug/cc.) prior to the albumin infusion. In each case the edematous tissue was removed at autopsy, digested in NaOH, and the total radioactive accumulation was determined. Autopsies were performed following all experiments and in several cases the pathway of the lymphatic drainage of the leg was traced. This was done by injecting 2 ml. of 4.0 per cent T-1824 dye directly into the cannulated lymphatic and sacrificing the animal after the dye appeared in the thoracic duct lymph. There appear to be two major pathways which the dye follows. One accompanies the femoral vein through the femoral ring into the pelvis and the other travels with the sciatic nerve and enters the pelvis in company with the inferior gluteal artery and vein. They then both join other pelvic and abdominal lymphatics to form the cisterna chyli. Thus, the infusion fluid passes through the popliteal, femoral, pelvic, and abdominal nodes. It also travels along sections of lymphatics consisting of vessels of very small and very large diameter.

The typical pattern of appearance of the labeled albumin in thoracic duct lymph is shown in Fig. 71. There is a time lag of approximately 10 minutes between the start of the infusion into the leg lymphatic and the appearance of measurable amounts of radioactive albumin in thoracic duct lymph. This is followed by an abrupt rise to a plateau which is maintained at an approximately constant level for the duration of the albumin infusion and for 10 minutes of the subsequent saline infusion. At that time, radioactivity in thoracic duct lymph falls sharply and continues to fall until the level approximates zero in about 140 to 150 minutes. Plasma radioactivity rises to a maximum concentration after 60 to 90 minutes and remains at this level for the remainder of the experiment. The maximum plasma concentration is less than 0.001 of the thoracic duct lymph concentration during its 50-minute plateau period.

Fig. 72 compares the cumulative albumin radioactivity in the infused

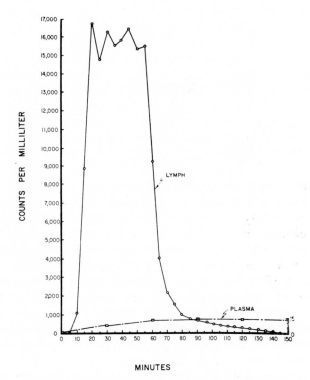

Fig. 71. Concentration of I^{131}-albumin in lymph and plasma. I^{131}-albumin solution infused centrally into leg lymphatic at zero time at rate of 0.5 ml./min. Albumin infusion stopped after 50 minutes and 0.9 per cent saline infusion started at same rate for next 100 minutes. All values are corrected for free I^{131} as described in text. The scale for lymph concentration is on left and that for plasma concentration is on right.

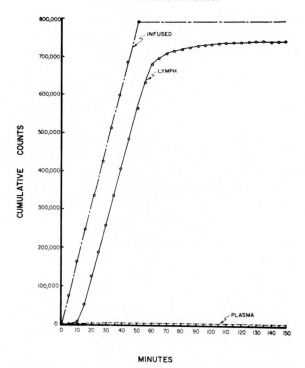

Fig. 72. The cumulative radioactive albumin in thoracic duct lymph and in the
plasma following infusion centrally into a leg lymphatic. Same experiment as Fig. 71.
All values are corrected for free I[131] as described in text.

albumin solution and that in thoracic duct lymph and plasma. Since the
albumin solution was infused at a constant rate, the curve expressing
its cumulative activity is a straight line with the slope being a measure
of the rate of infusion. It is important to note that the curve for cumulative radioactivity in lymph follows that of the infused fluid, showing
the 10-minute lag time as in Fig. 71 and reaching a plateau in 60 minutes, 10 minutes after the cessation of the albumin infusion and the start
of the saline infusion. The curve for cumulative activity of plasma is
also similar to that in Fig. 71.

It is apparent that the amount of albumin-bound radioactivity which
finds its way into plasma is extremely small as compared to the amount
found in thoracic duct lymph. The largest amount found was 2.29 per
cent of the injected dose. The average amount was 1.6 per cent. Since,
in the preparation of radioactive iodinated albumin, it is virtually impossible to remove all free iodine even after prolonged dialysis, the data
were analyzed to determine how much of the radioactivity of the lymph
and plasma could be ascribed to free iodine. Thus, we found that the

infusion solution contained an average of 97.8 per cent of protein-bound iodine and 2.2 per cent free iodine. Approximately the same distribution was found in the recovered radioactivity, 98.2 per cent being protein-bound and 1.8 per cent free iodine. As would be expected in view of the small molecular size of iodine, a greater fraction of the total amount of radioactivity in plasma was due to free iodine (average = 17 per cent) whereas only 1 per cent of the total radioactivity in thoracic duct lymph was in the unbound form.

The presence of edema in varying degrees in all experiments precluded a quantitative recovery of the infused radioactivity. As previously indicated, tissues that appeared edematous were removed and analyzed for radioactivity. From 4.2 to 15.6 per cent of the infused radioactivity was thus accounted for in different experiments. We could account for 100 per cent of the infused radioactivity in only one experiment. The average amount of radioactive albumin recovered in thoracic duct lymph was 54.4 per cent while 1.6 per cent was recovered in plasma. Analysis of lymph nodes perfused by the radioactive albumin showed no concentration of radioactivity in these organs greater than that expected from their blood content. The radioactive albumin not recovered is thought to be in edema fluid not analyzed or still in lymph vessels. In all experiments except two, where edema at the site of infusion was most marked, the percentage of protein-bound radioactivity recovered was greater than that of free iodine. The thoracic duct averaged 30.3 per cent of the free I^{131} while the plasma averaged 12.6 per cent of the free I^{131} infused. The average ratio of lymph to total plasma radioactive albumin is 35:1, whereby the ratio for free I^{131} is 2.4:1. The possibility exists, therefore, that small amounts of lymph albumin enter the circulation in passing through lymph nodes or lymph-blood vessel anastomoses other than the thoracic duct. An alternative explanation is that radioactive free iodine entered the circulation and subsequently became protein-bound. Analysis of the data indicates that the percentage of total radioactivity in the plasma as free I^{131} is between 1.3 and 1.5 times greater at 30 minutes than at 150 minutes. This is compatible with the assumption that radioactive free iodine moves more rapidly into the circulation than bound albumin, and it is possible that some of this may subsequently become bound to plasma proteins.

It is clear from our data that protein, once it gets into lymph ducts of the lower extremity, is returned virtually without loss to the venous circulation via the thoracic duct. However, they do not definitely deny direct exchange of serum albumin in lymph with that in blood vessels but indicate that if this does occur, it is very small in quantity. Lymph nodes apparently have little importance in the handling of albumin which has leaked from the vascular system, the albumin being returned virtually quantitatively to the blood stream via the main lymphatic channels.

This work is being continued, using dextrans of different molecular weights. We hope to go on to the use of electrolytes and other small molecules. We feel that a knowledge of the permeability of lymph ducts may be very helpful in interpreting fluid shifts between compartments as well as helping describe the functions of lymphatics.

REFERENCES

1. Wasserman, Karlman, and H. S. Mayerson. Dynamics of lymph and plasma protein exchange. Cardiologia. *21*:296-307 (1952).
2. Wasserman, Karlman, Leopold Loeb, and H. S. Mayerson. Capillary permeability to macromolecules. Circulation Res. *3*:594-603 (1955).
3. Yoffey, J. M., and F. C. Courtice. *Lymphatics, Lymph and Lymphoid Tissue.* Cambridge, Mass.: Harvard University Press, 1956, pp. 13-15.
4. Shirley, H. H., Jr., C. G. Wolfram, K. Wasserman, and H. S. Mayerson. Capillary permeability to macromolecules: stretched pore phenomenon. Amer. J. Physiol. *190*:189-93 (1957).
5. Patterson, Rodney M., Charles L. Ballard, Karlman Wasserman, and H.S. Mayerson. Lymphatic permeability to albumin. Amer. J. Physiol. *194*: 120-24 (1958).

DISCUSSION

CHAIRMAN FOWLER: Is there any discussion of this paper from the floor?

DR. CALLAHAN (Boston University): I would like to ask a little more about the free iodine in the tissues. This is, I suppose, iodine which has dissociated from the bound albumin to which it was originally bound. I am not quite sure that I heard correctly, but I believe you said that this free iodine distributes itself uniformly through the tissues of the body. If this is free iodine, is it taken up by the thyroid, or is there a differential concentration of this iodine in different tissues?

DR. LEO SAPIRSTEIN (Ohio State University School of Medicine): I would like to ask Dr. Mayerson if, in reporting the recovery of iodine or labeled plasma albumin in the lymph, he is recording this as the concentration ratio, or did he multiply by the plasma volume?

DR. MELVIN KNISELY: Dr. Mayerson asked for questions, and this is on microcirculation. The common concept today is that lymphatic vessels go to a lymph node, and the lymph then spreads through, some way or another, and comes out on the other end. In frogs, there are lymph hearts which pump directly from lymph vessels into veins, and you can watch them do it. I don't think anyone has ever ruled out the possibility that in a lymph node in a mammal, there may be machinery which pumps lymph directly from lymphatic to blood vessel. You certainly can't trust the histologists today to give you the answer.

CHAIRMAN FOWLER: I will ask Dr. Mayerson to close.

DR. MAYERSON: With regard to the first point, I think that I may have misled you. The point I was making here was that when we prepare the iodinated albumin, we get a firm combination of that protein which is tagged, that is, it does not break loose, at least within the time period that we are working in. You pretty well have to metabolize the protein. But I meant to indicate that no matter how careful you are in making your original solution of albumin, you don't get all the free iodine onto the albumin; that is, there is a certain percentage, about 1.5 per cent, roughly, of the iodine which remains unbound, and so, when you are infusing, you are infusing about 98.5 per cent bound iodine and about 1.5 per cent free.

I can't tell you if it distributes itself equally in all tissues, but from earlier work we do know that the free iodine does go particularly to the thyroid and the radioactive bound does not concentrate.

In answer to the second question of Dr. Sapirstein, as to whether we were working with concentrations or whether we used the plasma volume, we arbitrarily assumed the latter to be 5 per cent of the body weight and this value was used in calculating total radioactivity in the solution. We are reporting total radioactivity. We have no measure of lymph volumes or concentrations of the protein en route.

On Dr. Knisely's point of the lymph node acting as a pump, I know of no evidence suggesting this. We feel that, in many ways, the lymph capillaries can be regarded as functional continuations of the blood capillaries. We have some evidence to suggest this and I believe Dr. Sapirstein will also discuss this in the afternoon. We might, therefore, wait until then and discuss this in more detail.

CHAIRMAN FOWLER: The next presentation is by Dr. Murray C. Brown and Dr. Louise Warner on "Electronic Image Processing of Peripheral Vascular Beds."

ELECTRONIC IMAGE PROCESSING OF PERIPHERAL VASCULAR BEDS

Murray C. Brown and Louise Warner

National Heart Institute and *Georgetown University*

The group of instruments to which we have given the name "electronic image processors" are neither new nor newly introduced in biology. Kaufmann, Loeser, Parpart, Williams, Berkley, and many others have employed techniques derived from television to make valuable contributions to biological knowledge.

Our contribution has been the philosophic approach to these instruments. By characterizing the properties which they have in common and attempting to define the limiting parameters, we have hoped to interest an increasing number of biologists in their potential as methods of collecting and recording qualitative and quantitative data.

Electronic image processing is analogous to the more familiar optical image processing of which the phase microscope is a typical example. In that system, light which has passed through an image is processed within the microscope to present an image to the viewer's eye which is different from that observed in the ordinary microscope. The phase plate is the processing device which delays or accelerates that portion of the light which does not travel through a diffracting phase object. The two bundles of light are brought into phase to produce a diffraction pattern which the observer can see. In the electronic image processors the image is ultimately converted into an electronic signal which can then be processed by a variety of methods. The processed signal can then be presented to the viewer as an image resembling the original or in an altered form.

The cardinal qualities of these instruments are their ability to amplify light, contrast, and image size. Their secondary characteristics of greatest importance are the variety of methods of recording information, the range of spectral responses available, and the useful variables when color systems are used.

Today we are going to focus your attention on the potential value of light amplification and the motion picture recordings which are possible as one result of its use. If time permits, we may then briefly discuss one method of deriving quantitative information from the above system.

We were motivated to adapt the color television biomicroscope to a

136

reflecting system because of the interests of one of us in the study of the circulatory patterns in the human buccal mucous membrane and human gingiva. The conversion of the instrument itself was very simple, and consisted of substituting a standard ultropak illuminator for the microscope objective and eliminating the other equipment involved in the fused quartz rod transillumination procedure. The important question was whether satisfactory pictures could be made with the available level of illumination. We were reasonably sure that the heat produced in the tissue in this method would be well tolerated in most instances.

One of our colleagues is working with a standard cat brain preparation which is almost constantly available. He has experienced some difficulty in making adequate motion picture records. His interest in the possibility of using this instrument in his work provided an excellent opportunity for a convenient initial test. Here are the results of this trial run.

[Film]

The preparation consists of opening of the cat's skull over the parietal lobe of the brain under nembutal anesthesia. The dura remains intact until the experimental period starts. It is then quickly opened, the normal circulation is recorded for a few seconds, following which a standard cold injury is produced by application of a chilled plate for about 20 seconds. The film that we see shows these tissues at various periods during the experiment. It has no physiological significance because the experimental conditions were not maintained in this instance. It does demonstrate that the reflecting system works and that usable film records can be made. At the time we were concurrently testing methods of reducing the noise factor in our films and establishing standards for recording procedures. You will note that these films are much less noisy than our earlier pictures. It should be explained that the imperfections in the film seen as fixed spots are bits of dust attracted to the face of the camera tube by electrostatic forces. On this occasion the camera cooling system was not properly filtered. Aside from the fact that the ultropak light source contained almost no blue light, the system seemed entirely satisfactory. With a better spectral balance in the light source, good film recording should be possible at even lower light levels.

[Film stopped]

We then experimented with gum and buccal mucous membrane; the results were discouraging. Glare from mucous and saliva coupled with that from moist stratified squamous epithelium was a very serious problem. In our system, the problem of flare is intensified by the fact that the range of light level in a given field that can be reproduced on the screen is relatively limited. While there are other advantages in the use of this instrument, it seemed that flare would present a problem requiring more manipulation of the biological material than did photography.

We then examined the possibility that these tissues could be seen and recorded with a simpler electronic system. This is the flying spot scanning microscope. It is not a new instrument, having been first designed by Zworykin in the early twenties. For a long time there was no biological interest in the instrument because of the extremely limited amount of light available. It also has the disadvantage that it must be operated in total darkness. In recent years, interest in this device as a transilluminating microscope has been growing. Research applications of this system by Williams and Montgomery, who are interested in ultraviolet absorption spectra, Loeser, who has studied the absorption patterns of biological material in the visible spectra, and by others has yielded important information. There has been less interest in its possibilities as a reflecting microscope, no studies as yet having come to our attention.

If the problem of packaging the instrument in a convenient form can be overcome, and the hazards of the high voltages employed in the sensing device could be safeguarded, there seems no reason why modern supersensitive detectors could not make a reflecting system work. The basic instrument is simple in concept and fortunately recently became obsolete in the commercial form which was developed for the television broadcast industry. The latter point is important. Existence of cheap used equipment greatly simplifies the construction of the instrument. We obtained a black-and-white version of the broadcast instrument this winter in order to test the possibility of its use as a reflecting microscope. The instrument consists of a light source which is a special cathode ray tube. Light from this tube is projected through a microscope lens system and comes to focus upon the subject matter under view. One or more photomultiplier tubes view the light reflected from the subject matter and convert it into an electrical signal which after great amplification is sent to a television picture tube. The trick that makes this system work is the fact that the dancing spot of light projected on the subject travels in exact synchronization with the electron beam in the television picture tube. The amount of reflected light seen by the photomultiplier tube at any instant in time is immediately reported to the television picture tube as the degree of brightness seen by the photomultiplier. The picture on the television tube can be photographed by a variety of motion picture cameras.

To make this into a reflecting microscope we employed readily available optical equipment. An ultropak objective was attached to a monocular microscope barrel and so placed that it could view the cathode ray tube. A tiny supersensitive Dumont photomultiplier tube was available that almost exactly fits the ultropak illuminator attachment fitting. The combination of these elements was not difficult, although some problems of cable length interfered with our first attempts to use the system. These were overcome. The resolution of the new arrangement was tested and seemed to approximate that of motion picture film. At this point, the experiment was abandoned. The special cathode ray tube required for our unit imploded with considerable noise and distributed shards about the laboratory and a wonderful collection of splinters in the ultropak. We had overreached ourselves by providing a wonderful optical enclosure for the CRO light path to the microscope at the expense of heat dissipation from the CRO tube. Tubes to fit every other existing flying spot scanner were available at modest prices, but ours would have to be built by hand on special order. Through the kindness of the industry, two tubes have now been found and given to us. Further results will have to await their arrival.

There is good reason to believe, on the basis of our limited observation as well as theory, that this device has a place in microcirculatory studies. The light which reaches the tissue is not only low in intensity, but also carries little heat. The reflected light need not be observed by the sensing device at the angle of incidence to the tissue, but, by appropriate physical arrangement can be the light reflected obliquely at any chosen angle. The image reproduced on the screen can be the view seen at the angle of incidence or highlighted by any degree of oblique reflection one wishes. It is likely that this will solve the problem of flare from moist and highly reflective surfaces. At present, sources are available that provide ultraviolet and visible light spectra, making studies of fluorescence and visualization of color possible. The only limitation which must be added to those already mentioned is the fact that the photomultiplier tube senses total light present. This means that no usable information can be obtained unless the reflected light from the tiny flying spot or from any excited state of material in the subject matter is immediately quenched when the spot moves on to its next contiguous position. To its advantage can be added the fact that the system is inherently linear, which to us biologists means it does not readily introduce artifacts.

The possibilities for making physical measurements as by line selection and reflection are the same as for any television system.

Since 1955, when we visualized and recorded (in black and white) the circulation in the retina of a sighted human eye for the first time, we have felt that motion picture records of the retinal arterial and venous circulation in color could be extremely valuable. This circulation is the only completely undisturbed yet accessible vascular bed in man. Of equal importance, it is also a sample of the carotid arterial supply to the brain.

Any photography of this vascular bed presents formidable problems.

The pupillary aperture limits the effective aperture of any viewing system, the choroid absorbs light very effectively, the retina tolerates incident light poorly, and the curved field imposes further optical problems. At comfortable light levels the sighted eye cannot be photographed satisfactorily; and the higher light levels required for motion pictures are not tolerable.

In November of 1957 Dr. A. M. Potts[1] reported to the Academy of Ophthalmology our joint success in visualizing the retina with a color television system. After citing the obvious usefulness of this technique for teaching, Dr. Potts said:

In addition, color values may be purposely distorted to better demonstrate a particular lesion. The classical view with so-called "red-free light" may now be truly monochromatic thanks to the availability of interference filters and the sensitivity of the television tube. Indeed by color translation techniques, wave lengths in the ultraviolet and infra-red invisible to the unaided eye may be utilized for examination and appear in color on the television screen.

There are a number of research applications which are of value. Using a series of monochromatic filters one could actually measure the absorption spectrum of a lesion as an aid to categorizing it. By selecting a single line electronically from the television picture one can display blood vessel diameters as peaks and valleys on a cathode ray oscilloscope screen and record the dynamic changes in these dimensions on magnetic tape for later analysis. Thus vasospastic disease and pharmacodynamics of vasomotor drugs may be studied with facility.

The heart of our system is the newly developed 73469 research image orthicon tube of RCA combined with the CBS color camera used in the biomicroscope. When these in turn are combined with a retinal camera or indeed with only the objective lens of such a camera and with a suitable low-level light source the retina can be viewed. The camera tube has a quantum efficiency approaching 20 per cent, which is the greatest sensitivity yet achieved. Our first pictures were made with the illumination of the standard hand-held ophthalmoscope. Lately, the Bausch and Lomb camera was used with a heavily filtered zirconium arc light source. The level of illumination is that used for focusing preparatory to making still photographs. It is well tolerated for long periods of time. The instrument is so simple to use that our colleague, W. C. Whitehouse, aligns himself while watching the monitor with the opposite eye.

Films made for Dr. James Toole as part of a motion picture film to teach the technique of ophthalmodynamometry for the identification of carotid artery occlusion will now be shown. You will see the veins on the disc begin to pulsate as the dynamometer is applied, then the arterial pulsation as the pressure of this spring-loaded gauge is increased to produce an intraocular tension equivalent to the diastolic blood pressure.

[1] Potts, A. M., and M. C. Brown. A color television ophthalmoscope. Amer. Acad. Ophthal. and Otol. Jan.-Feb., 1958, p. 136.

Finally, the arteries on the disc blanch as the systolic level is reached. This is the first formal showing of the first color motion picture of the retinal circulation in a sighted human eye.

[Film]

Here we see the instrument. Here is the camera containing the super-sensitive RCA tube which looks at the retinal camera through a color wheel which we cannot see. Light from the zirconium arc passes through filters and prisms and then the objective lens and into the eye. The reflected light travels back through the same lens to the camera lens and then through the color wheel to the camera tube.

Here is the eye as the dynamometer is applied. Then the pressure increases, veins pulsate, then the artery at diastolic. The gauge is read and reapplied. Now systolic pressure is reached. Now the entire procedure is repeated. This is the work print for Dr. Toole's film. The original was made during the period when we had standardized an emulsion and exposure but before the technique to reduce noise had been developed. In view of the imminence of the various spring meetings, retakes of this film were deferred.

The film has one characteristic which puzzles us. On examination of individual frames it is found to be much less noisy than when projected. The scintillation between red and yellow is the product of differences other than random noise between successive frames. We believe it is probably due to the combination of the way in which the film produces these two colors, and the method whereby the color monitor produces them, because this does not occur with color combinations. This is being investigated.

Finally, we would like to show you a slide or two. First, an example of how spectral sensitivity can be helpful. You will note there is a ropey, bluish pattern in the upper left of the field with a roughly vascular distribution. This is the eye of a man with a primary melanoma on his forearm and known metastasis to the brain proper. This lesion could not be seen on ophthalmoscopic examination even after it was recorded through the television system. Our ability to see it on the screen is due to the fact the camera tube sees green and yellow much better than the eye and their absorption is therefore more evident.

DISCUSSION

CHAIRMAN FOWLER: This paper is now open for general discussion. Do we have any discussion of this very interesting paper?

DR. MELVIN KNISELY: I have just one question. It is certainly excellent work. One of the great difficulties of all studies of circulation is the tremendous light necessary, which often overheats the patient. There is the problem of glare. Higginbotham in our laboratory began to use polarized light, which got rid of a lot of the glare. Murray, did you try to use polarized light?

Dr. Brown: Not yet.

Dr. Dunham (Medical College of South Carolina): I would like to ask how many lines per inch or how many lines were in the screen that you used, and I would also like to know whether or not you have experimented with any of the very high frequency light or ultrashortwavelength light, in, say, the ultraviolet region, in so far as improving the resolution of the light system goes.

Dr. Brown: The inherent limitation of the system which you saw here is the fact that it has 405 lines from top to bottom of the screen. This, however, is not as much of a limitation as you might think. We can produce, with this system, 600-line average resolution at least. That is, you can distinguish 600 lines in a space equivalent to that between the top and bottom of the screen. The limitation of the 16 mm. colored motion picture film is 495 lines or 500 lines, so you can exceed, under ideal conditions, this limitation. Horizontal resolution is very good while vertical resolution is less good.

As to using other light systems, I don't think we gain too much in these applications. The sensing instrument we are using has the same spectrum as the human eye. We have used tubes with spectra that are sensitive to infrared, and, with those, we can do tricks like identifying, absorbing, and transmitting materials like hemoglobin. I don't think that the special light sources would gain us too much in studies of microcirculation because most of our usual sources contain light of the wave lengths useful to our studies.

In the pictures that were made here, incidentally, the tube is another element that goes into the resolution. The picture you saw on the screen was made up of two red scans, two green scans, and one blue, so there is a total of five pictures in each frame of motion picture, and this has its own effect.

Dr. Melvin Knisely: Wouldn't it be possible to do spectrophotographic analysis of the venous blood in the retina and determine the oxygen concentration of venous blood and thereby the retinal metabolism?

Dr. Brown: You can do it within limits with this system. If we can use the flying spot scanner as we hope, we can probably do it rather precisely. In the present system the limitation is bleeding from color field to color field, of which there is not much but there is some. This limits the accuracy of the absorption studies.

Dr. Knisely: You show a sharp contrast between arterial and venous blood color there.

DR. BROWN: Oh, that's true, but if you are going to quantitate it, the problem is that you have a system which is not entirely linear.

DR. KNISELY: Can you find a curve?

DR. BROWN: You can get a rough idea of what is going on.

CHAIRMAN FOWLER: I regret that we are well over our time now, and the anchor man is coming up. I will now introduce Dr. Zweifach of New York University–Bellevue Medical Center.

Structural and Functional Aspects of the Microcirculation in the Skin

Benjamin W. Zweifach

New York University–Bellevue Medical Center

Most of our information concerning the circulation in the skin has been derived either from anatomical reconstructions(1, 2) or from indirect measurements of blood flow(3, 4). Neither of these methods has provided an adequate representation of the functional characteristics of the microcirculation, particularly with respect to the prominent venous plexus in the skin. The direct observational approach affords the unique opportunity of directly relating structure and functional behavior in the same set of vessels. Numerous studies have been made on the skin circulation in man(5), but these permit visualization of only limited capillary loops. Work in this area in experimental animals has been confined to the larger blood vessels of accessible structures such as the ear(6) or in flaps of skin(7). Successful visualization of the microcirculation in skeletal muscle after careful surgical preparation(8) encouraged us to attempt a similar approach for the small blood vessels of the skin.

It was clearly apparent that the most profitable means of viewing the cutaneous circulation in its entirety would be from the undersurface. A surgical technique was therefore devised whereby a flap of skin in the rat could be folded back and meticulously cleaned of its adhering connective tissue. The exposed undersurface was then irrigated with a gelatin-Ringer's solution at body temperature and transilluminated by draping the skin over a lucite rod which also acted as a condenser for the illuminating system. After completing the observations on the living circulation, an opaque suspension of carbon in gelatin was injected and the specimen fixed *in situ*. Details of the structural arrangement of these small vessels in the same skin site could thereby be filled in.

Our classical concepts of the manner in which the larger blood vessels subdivide to form the terminal vascular bed have undergone considerable revision during recent years. Current studies show that instead of branching repeatedly to form successively smaller units, the smaller ramifications of the arterial vessels exhibit a regular pattern of interconnecting links, particularly in the connective tissue between the skin and underlying skeletal muscle. From this coarse network arises a series of small arteries

144

(100 μ) which, as they enter the skin proper, repeatedly interconnect to form an extensive meshwork of long arterioles about 50 μ in diameter. The arrangement of the interdigitating arterioles serves to demarcate discrete areas of tissue which are supplied with blood by twigs from the interarteriolar network. The resulting appearance is very much like the rungs of a ladder, the center of which consists of a secondary network of fine capillary vessels. The capillary bed proper is thus made up of precapillary and capillary vessels which are branches of the interarcading arterioles and dichotomize in the conventional manner.

The effluent flow from the capillary bed is collected into wide tributaries which in turn join to form the first portion of the venous system, the collecting venules. These venules then become linked with one another in the subcutaneous tissue to make up an interarcading plexus similar to, but even more extensive than, the associated network of arterial vessels. Many of the arteriolar branches, after a short course, return directly into the venous circulation. Less frequent, but still significant, are direct connections between arterial and venous plexuses, so that blood can be shunted to the venous side without traversing the network of capillaries. Proportionately, the venous circulation is by far the major segment of the cutaneous vasculature.

From a structural aspect, the branches emanating from the arterial arcades resemble the "metarterioles" in other tissues(9) in possessing a thin, closely applied layer of smooth muscle. These branches are distinguished by their comparatively straight course, forming a structure very much like the trunk of a tree from which numerous offshoots are distributed successively until the vessel loses its identity in the capillary bed proper. The side channels are the precapillaries, which are characterized by the presence of coiled or spirally arranged muscle cells in the immediate junctional region. The precapillary vessels in the skin show the characteristic spontaneous vasomotion which is so striking at this level of organization in other tissues. Occasional precapillaries are distributed directly from the larger arterial plexuses and enter the dermis proper. Although these long slender branches are comparatively infrequent, they are however functionally important, since they continue to supply blood to scattered areas of the skin under conditions where active shunts have opened up to bypass the majority of skin capillaries.

Direct observations reveal that the number of vessels with an active circulation changes intermittently without relation to the irregular vasomotor excursions of the deeper arterioles and venules. It is noteworthy that the small venules show a continuous, almost rhythmic pattern of spontaneous activity in the skin in contrast to their relative inactivity in most tissues. As in other tissues, the structural evolution of the capillary bed is paralleled by a gradient in the responsiveness or reactivity of the muscular components to stimuli(1). In the cutaneous circulation, the arteriole-to-arteriole arcades are exceptionally responsive to constrictor and dilator agents. With minimal or threshold stimuli, the arcades close down first and, as a result, trap blood in the network. The venous network is greatly influenced by changes in temperature, showing as much as a ten to twenty fold increase in the constrictor response to epinephrine or norepinephrine when the temperature falls as little as 1° or 2° C. Although the vascular bed in other tissues is also affected by fluctuations in temperature, the venous network in the skin represents a unique structure in this regard.

Studies on the functional behavior of the cutaneous circulation were made in two ways. In one set of experiments, the tissue was prepared for microcirculatory observations, and vasoactive substances were applied locally. In a second set of experiments, the local response to vasoactive agents was measured by the extent to which albumin-bound Evans blue permeated from the bloodstream into a skin site pretreated with selected mediators. A number of representative experiments will be cited to indicate the application of these techniques.

In recent years we have focused attention on the over-all manifestations of bacterial endotoxins, partly because of the extraordinary scope of their biological properties, and partly because the approach provided a useful experimental tool for analyzing the regulatory mechanisms of the skin circulation. It was early recognized(11) that many of the vascular effects produced by bacterial extracts were similar to those produced by epinephrine. For example, it has been found that the dermal hemorrhagic lesions of the Schwartzman type, produced by successive doses of bacterial endotoxins in the rabbit, could be duplicated by combinations of epinephrine and endotoxin. The conventional lesion of dermal necrosis is elicited in the rabbit by two appropriately spaced injections of bacterial extracts, the first in the skin, and the second intravenously about 18 to 20 hours later. The same type of extensive dermal necrosis or hemorrhage could be produced by the administration of endotoxin systemically followed by the local injection of epinephrine into the skin(12). Mixtures of epinephrine and endotoxin injected into the skin likewise led to a hemorrhagic lesion, despite the fact that epinephrine by itself, even when injected repeatedly for a period up to six hours into a given site, did not elicit a comparable reaction.

Direct observations of the circulation in the skin have revealed that in both the local Schwartzman type of lesion and in the systemic reaction to endotoxin, there was an exaggerated response of the small blood vessels to epinephrine or norepinephrine. Thus, threshold doses of epinephrine produced in the endotoxin-treated animal a severe vasoconstriction and when repeated several times, lead to capillary stasis and local hemorrhage.

Both of the basic structural components of the vascular tree, the smooth muscle and endothelial cells, were found to be involved in the endotoxin lesion. Initially, only the responsiveness and tone of the smooth muscle elements were affected. This circumstance in turn led to a disruption of local blood flow concomitant with progressive endothelial damage involving capillary stasis and petechial hemorrhage. Direct visual studies have revealed that the altered pattern of reactivity involved not only the feeding arterioles, but also the venular arcades. Following systemic endotoxin, the venules showed a heightened reactivity to the extent that normally threshold amounts of epinephrine served to produce an unrelieved narrowing, often for as long as 30 to 40 minutes. As the endotoxic state continued, the pattern of reactivity shifted and arteriolar and precapillary dilation developed concurrent with signs of endothelial damage.

In searching for an explanation for the local disturbances following endotoxin, the possibility was entertained that the effects on vascular reactivity might be mediated by the release of vasoactive agents from the tissue. Various tissue mediators, including histamine and 5-hydroxytryptamine (5-HT) have been suggested(13). Our own work has led us to implicate the amine, serotonin or 5-HT, which is widely distributed in most tissues and has been shown to be released during various forms of stress. Although neither 5-HT nor epinephrine by themselves led to local tissue damage, the local administration of mixtures of these two amines produced the cardinal symptoms of dermal necrosis and capillary petechiae. Direct observational studies revealed that mixtures made up of as little as 1 μg epinephrine and 2 μg 5-HT, induced widespread damage to the capillary endothelium, and eventual stasis. The characteristic venospasm previously described for endotoxin was regularly encountered with this mixture of amines. Damage to the endothelium could be clearly demonstrated by injecting colloidal carbon and noting the sequestration of the particles by injured endothelial elements.

The seemingly selective action of mixtures of epinephrine and 5-HT on venous smooth muscle suggests that the simultaneous presence of both amines interferes with a common enzyme system for handling these amines. Thus, the local liberation of 5-HT could be conceived to saturate an enzyme such as monamine oxidase and thereby interfere with the inactivation of epinephrine. With the continued presence of increased amounts of 5-HT, the receptor sites on the smooth muscle would become occupied by this agent and thereby serve to prevent the reaction with epinephrine or norepinephrine.

The basis for the endothelial damage is not readily apparent. There are reports that 5-HT alters the intracellular handling of sodium(14). It is therefore possible that the stimulating action of epinephrine on carbohydrate metabolism of cells, which have taken up sodium through the action of 5-HT, will result in endothelial damage.

Experiments in which animals were made resistant or tolerant to the effects of bacterial endotoxins have a bearing on this concept. Tolerance to endotoxin could be induced by repeated injections of bacterial extracts over a period of 5 to 10 days. In such animals, none of the vascular sequelae of endotoxemia are observed either with systemic or local administration(15). In normal animals receiving endotoxin, the repeated administration of constrictor doses of epinephrine led to capillary damage. In tolerant rats, the cutaneous vessels showed no untoward effects, even with excessive amounts of epinephrine. Perhaps the most significant observation was the fact that mixtures of epinephrine and 5-HT were no longer vasotoxic. They did not produce endothelial damage, although there was a modest increase in the reactivity of the smooth muscle elements to constrictor stimuli.

In the past(16), the evolution of a local dermal lesion was studied by the sequestration of a circulating colored colloidal complex (usually T-1824 or Trypan blue) into the site, with the intensity of the coloration serving as a measure of the altered vascular permeability. Although various attempts have been made to quantitate the reaction, none of the proposed methods proved adequate or reproducible. In the present experiments, a quantitative index of the local phenomenon was achieved by introducing into a series of skin sites successively diluted doses of the agent and noting the threshold concentration below which no blue wheal developed.

In view of the similarity of the endotoxin reaction and that induced by epinephrine on blood vessels, the initial studies were concerned with the mode of interaction of epinephrine and endotoxin on the local response to vasoactive agents.

In Table 4 are listed the threshold concentrations of four different agents used to induce local vascular damage. It can be seen that the skin is extraordinarily sensitive to agents, such as acetylcholine (Ach) and 5-hydroxytryptamine (5-HT), with the latter producing a change in vascular permeability at concentrations as low as 10^{-10} μg/ml. The first series of experiments was conducted to determine whether any of these important tissue mediators were implicated in the systemic response to bacterial endotoxins. The skin reactions were studied one hour after moderate doses (25 to 100 μg) of an *E. coli* preparation had been administered intraperitoneally. It is significant that the vascular effects of all of the local mediators were blunted to some extent, so that much

TABLE 4. VASCULAR EFFECTS OF ENDOTOXIN AS TESTED BY
LOCAL SKIN REACTIONS TO VASOACTIVE AGENTS

Pretreatment	Threshold Values of Local Test Substances		
	Ach μg./ml	Histamine μg./ml	5-HT μg./ml
Controls	0.5	1.5	1×10^{-10}
Epinephrine (s.c.)			
5 μg.	0.5	1.5	10^{-9}
10 μg.	5.0	2.0	10^{-7}
20 μg.	>100	10.0	$>10^{-2}$
E. coli endotoxin (i.p.)*			
10 μg.	0.5	1.5	$>10^{-6}$
50 μg.	>100	1.5	$>10^{-2}$
200 μg.	>100	15.0	$>10^{-2}$
Epinephrine (5 μg.)			
After endotoxin (10 μg.)	>100	1.5	$>10^{-2}$

* Endotoxin-treated rats tested at 1 hour.

higher concentrations were required to produce a threshold reaction. This finding is in accord with the previously advanced concept that endotoxin involves the vascular interaction with epinephrine, since the injection of 5 to 10 μg of this amine had an identical effect on the local skin bluing with the four tissue mediators being studied. Further corroboration of the role of epinephrine in the response to bacterial extracts was obtained in experiments on rats pretreated with adrenergic blockers, such as dibenzyline or benodaine. Following blockade, there was no shift in local tissue reactivity to the test agents when endotoxin was given in amounts up to 200 μg. The above experiments, in conjunction with studies on antihistamines, cholinergic blockers, etc., have led us to conclude that a basic feature of local tissue regulation of blood flow is the interdependence of local tissue amines and systemic epinephrine or norepinephrine.

CONCLUSIONS

The structural make-up of the cutaneous circulation is atypical since it represents a predominantly venous network of vessels and is unusually responsive to fluctuations in temperature, and amines other than epinephrine or norepinephrine. The circulation in the skin would appear to be regulated either directly through the release of 5-HT, or through a secondary effect resulting from the local accumulation of such amines. The suggestion has been advanced that the reaction involves also the release of either epinephrine or norepinephrine, and hence is probably dependent on neurohumoral factors. The local release of tissue mediators implies a direct action upon the constituents of the small vessels and/or an indirect effect arising from an interference with the enzymes responsible for removing these mediators from the tissue.

REFERENCES

1. Spalteholz, W. Die Verteilung der Blutgefaesse im Muskel. Abh. sächs. Ges. (akad.) Wiss. *14*:509-78 (1888).
2. Redisch, W., F. F. Tangoo, and R. L. de C. Saunders, *Peripheral Circulation in Health and Disease*. New York: Grune & Stratton, 1957.
3. Lewis, Thomas. *The Blood Vessels of the Human Skin and Their Responses*. London: Shaw, 1927.
4. Kerslake, D. McK., and K. E. Copper. "Factors concerned in the regulation of skin blood flow" in *Peripheral Circulation in Man*. Ciba Foundation Symposium. Boston: Little, Brown & Co., 1954.
5. Burton, A. C. "A critical survey of methods available for the measurement of human peripheral blood flow" in *Peripheral Circulation in Man*. Ciba Foundation Symposium. Boston: Little, Brown & Co., 1954.
6. Armin, J., R. T. Grant, E. H. S. Thompson, and A. Tickner. An explanation for the heightened vascular reactivity of the denervated rabbit's ear. J. Physiol. *121*:603-22 (1953).
7. Algire, G. H., and R. M. Merwin. Vascular patterns in tissues and grafts within transparent chambers in mice. Angiology. *6*:311-18 (1955).
8. Zweifach, B. W., and D. B. Metz. Selective distribution of blood through the terminal vascular bed of mesenteric structures and skeletal muscle. Angiology. *6*:282-90 (1955).
9. Zweifach, B. W. "Basic mechanisms in peripheral vascular homeostasis" in *Factors Regulating Blood Pressure*. Third Conference, Josiah Macy, Jr. Foundation, 1949, p. 13.
10. Zweifach, B. W. General principles governing the behavior of the microcirculation. Amer. J. Med. *23*:684-96 (1957).
11. Delaunay, A., P. Boquet, J. Lebrun, Y. Lehoult, and M. Delaunay. Le mode d'action des endotoxins bacteriennes; les troubles vaso-moteurs chex les animaux intoxiquès et leur consequences. J. Physiol. (Paris) *40*:89-110 (1948).
12. Thomas, L. The role of adrenalin in the reactions produced by the endotoxins of gram-genative bacteria. I. Hemorrhagic necrosis produced by adrenalin in the skin of endotoxin-treated rabbits. J. exp. Med. *104*:865-80 (1956).
13. Parratt, J. R., and G. B. West. 5-Hydroxytryptamine and tissue mast cells. J. Physiol. *137*:169-78 (1957).
14. Page, I. H. Serotonin (5-Hydroxytryptamine); the last four years. Physiol. Rev. *38*:277-335 (1958).
15. Zweifach, B. W., and L. Thomas. The relationship between the vascular manifestations of shock produced by endotoxin, trauma and hemorrhage. I. Certain similarities between the reaction in normal and endotoxin-tolerant rats. J. exp. Med. *106*:385-401 (1957).
16. Menkin, V. *Biochemistry of Inflammation*. New York: Macmillan Co., 1956.
17. Ovary, T., and Briot, M. Nouvelle méthode de dosage de l'anticorps anaphylactique et son rapport avec l'azote de l'anticorps. Ann. Inst. Pasteur. *81*:670-73 (1951).

DISCUSSION

CHAIRMAN FOWLER: This presentation is now open for general discussion. Are there any questions?

DR. MELVIN KNISELY: A tremendous number of papers have been published by microcirculatory people talking about circulation in membranes. The only reason for studying the thin membrane is because it is easy to get light through it so you can see it.

One of the characteristics of thin membranes, wherever you find them, is that they are pretty much connective tissue, so, by and large, an awful lot of literature is based upon studying the vascular apparatus of extremely simple connective tissue. In 1940 I wrote a paper very carefully pointing out that the architecture of vascular beds was the function of the organ itself—both the architecture and the physiology of the organ. I have a wonderful set of reprints that nobody ever asked for at all!

In 1954, Sanders and I published a paper in which we listed a very large sample of all the internal organs which could be studied by transillumination or reflected light, including things like thyroid, in which Walter Medill saw arteriovenous anastomoses in the dog, in a whole raft of organs. Sam Reynolds has been studying uterus. Certainly, the vascular apparatus is totally different from any mesentery that I happen to know about.

I think that we have to extend this and talk about species. In an organ like skin, it will be necessary to talk about individual areas, because, in human beings, there is good anatomical evidence of large numbers of big arterial anastomoses along the side of the fingers. I haven't seen any papers on the vascular apparatus of the shoulder blade. Certainly, handling it at temperatures is quite different from extremities in the body. Rhesus monkeys have enormous numbers of great big arterial anastomoses on the inside of the eyelids, and when human beings freeze in cold temperatures, the eyelids are one of the last things to freeze.

I myself long ago quit thinking about generalizing. I think that the study of an organ should be related to the organ itself, whether it is spleen, liver, or striated muscle. I think that it has to be limited by the species about which we are talking. If you generalize beyond that, you have an unhappy time.

CHAIRMAN FOWLER: Are there any other questions from the floor? If not, I will ask Dr. Zweifach to close.

DR. ZWEIFACH: I have closed, as far as I am concerned.

CHAIRMAN FOWLER: Dr. Reynolds has a few remarks that he wants to make before we recess for luncheon.

DR. REYNOLDS: I want to thank Dr. Fowler for his very able chairing of the session this morning. He is, as you know, your chairman for the conference next year. I think that now you all know him very well, and can look forward to the meeting next year, wherever it is going to be.

[The session recessed at twelve-forty o'clock.]

MICROCIRCULATORY CONFERENCE, 1958 *

Abramson, Dr. David I., Department of Physical Medicine and Rehabilitation, University of Illinois College of Medicine, 1853 West Polk St., Chicago 12, Ill.

Akers, Dr. Robert P., National Heart Institute, Bethesda 14, Md.

*Allen, Dr. Lane, Medical College of Georgia, University Place, Augusta, Ga.

Allison, Dr. Fred B., Department of Medicine, University of Mississippi School of Medicine, Jackson, Miss.

Anderson, Dr. James M., Department of Pathology, University of Minnesota Medical School, Minneapolis, Minn.

Anderson, Dr. Rupert S., Chemical Corps Medical Laboratories, Army Medical Center, Md.

Arendt, Dr. Kenneth A., Department of Physiology, College of Medical Evangelists, Loma Linda, Calif.

*Arnold, Dr. John D., Department of Medicine, University of Chicago College of Medicine, Chicago 37, Ill.

*Bacon, Dr. R. L., University of Oregon Medical School, Portland 1, Ore.

*Baez, Dr. Silvio, Department of Anesthesiology, New York University–Bellevue, Medical Center, 550 First Ave., New York 16, N.Y.

*Barclay, Dr. William R., University of Chicago, 950 East 59th St., Chicago 37, Ill.

*Baringer, Dr. J. Richard, Western Reserve University School of Medicine, Cleveland 6, Ohio

*de Beer, Dr. E. J., Wellcome Research Laboratories, Tuckahoe, N. Y.

*Bellman, Dr. Ben, Beth Israel Hospital, 330 Brookline Ave., Boston 15, Mass.

Benditt, Dr. Earl P., Department of Pathology, University of Chicago, Chicago 37, Ill.

*Berman, Dr. Herbert J., Department of Biology, Boston University, Boston 15, Mass.

Bigelow, Dr. W. C., Department of Surgery, University of Toronto, Toronto, Canada

*Blanding, Dr. Douglas, Medical College of South Carolina, Charleston, S. C.

*Bloch, Dr. Edward H., Department of Anatomy, Western Reserve University School of Medicine, Cleveland, Ohio

* Those indicated by an asterisk were present at the Buffalo meeting.

153

Bohr, Dr. David F., Physiology Laboratory, University of Michigan, Ann Arbor, Mich.

*Brenner, Dr. Robert M., Brown University, Providence, R. I.

*Brown, Dr. M. C., National Heart Institute, Bethesda 14, Md.

*Bruce, Dr. W. R., University of Chicago College of Medicine, Department of Medicine, Chicago 37, Ill.

Buckley, Dr. Nancy M., Department of Physiology, Albert Einstein College of Medicine, East Chester Rd. and Morris Park Ave., New York 61, N. Y.

*Burrage, Dr. W. S., Massachusetts General Hospital, Boston, Mass.

Burton, Dr. Alan C., Department of Biophysics, University of Western Ontario, London, Ontario, Canada

*Butler, Dr. Robert, University of Chicago, Chicago 37, Ill.

*Callahan, Dr. Arthur B., Boston University, 15 Elmwood St., Newton, Mass.

Clark, Dr. Elinor, Wistar Institute, Philadelphia, Pa.

Clark, Dr. Eliot R., Wistar Institute, Philadelphia, Pa.

Clarkson, Dr. Thomas B., Research Dept., Massengill Company, Bristol, Tenn.

*Conway, Dr. Anna M., St. Louis University, St. Louis 4, Mo.

Copeland, Dr. Eugene, Division Research Grants, National Institute of Health, Bethesda 14, Md.

Copley, Dr. A., Medical Research Laboratories, Charing Cross Hospital, 8 Exchange Court, Strand, London W.C. 2, England.

Corcoran, Dr. A. C., Cleveland Clinic, Cleveland, Ohio

*Craig, Dr. Robert L., G. D. Searle & Co., Chicago, Ill.

Crismon, Dr. J. M., Department of Physiology, Stanford University, Stanford, Calif.

Culbertson, Dr. James W., State University of Iowa, Iowa City, Iowa

Cunningham, Dr. George J., Royal College of Surgeons, Lincoln's Inn Fields, London W.C. 2, England

Curri, Dr. Sergio B., Via Marcona 70, Milan, Italy

Daiell, Dr. H. L., Lakeside Laboratories, Milwaukee, Wis.

*Darby, Dr. Elinor, National Heart Institute, Bethesda 14, Md.

Davis, Dr. Darrel, Department of Physiology, Medical College of Georgia, University Place, Augusta, Ga.

*Ditzel, Dr. Jørn, Harvard Medical School, 5 Taft Ave., West Newton, Mass.

*Dunahue, Dr. Fred W., Department of Anatomy, Medical College, University of Vermont, Burlington, Vt.

*Dunham, Mrs. F. Harding, Medical College of South Carolina, Station 27, Sullivans Island, S. C.

*Dunham, Dr. William H., Medical College of South Carolina, Station 27, Sullivans Island, S. C.

Dustan, Dr. Harriet, Cleveland Clinic, Cleveland, Ohio

Ebert, Dr. R. H., Department of Medicine, Western Reserve University School of Medicine, Cleveland 6, Ohio

Eckman, Dr. Philip L., Department of Pathology, University of Minnesota, Minneapolis, Minn.

*Eddy, Dr. Hubert A., Atomic Energy Project, Rochester 20, N. Y.

Eichna, Dr. Ludwig W., Department of Medicine, New York University–Bellevue Medical Center, 550 First Ave., New York 16, N. Y.

*Eliot, Dr. T. S., 4200 East 9th Ave., Denver, Colo.

Essex, Dr. Hiram, Division of Experimental Medicine, Mayo Foundation, Rochester, Minn.

Farber, Dr. Eugene M., Stanford University School of Medicine, Division of Dermatology, Stanford University Hospitals, San Francisco 15, Calif.

*Fawcett, Dr. Don W., Cornell Medical College, York Ave. and 68th St., New York, N. Y.

Feinsilver, Dr. Oscar, 390 Main St., Worcester, Mass.

Fine, Dr. Jacob, Beth Israel Hospital, 330 Brookline Ave., Boston 15, Mass.

Fleming, Dr. Thomas C., Medical Research Laboratories, Mead Johnson & Co., Evansville 21, Ind.

Florey, Dr. R. W., Dunn School of Pathology, Oxford University, Oxford, England

*Fowler, Dr. Edmund P., Jr., Department of Otolaryngology, College of Physicians and Surgeons, Columbia University, 180 Fort Washington Ave., New York, N. Y.

Freis, Dr. Edward D., Veterans Administration Hospital, 2650 Wisconsin Ave., N.W., Washington, D.C.

Fulton, Dr. George P., Biology Department, Boston University, Boston, Mass.

Ganley, Dr. Oswald H., Department of Bacteriology, Merck Sharp & Dohme, West Point, Pa.

Gaudino, Dr. Mario, Abbott Laboratories International, Merchandise Mart Plaza, Chicago 54, Ill.

*Gillilan, Dr. Lois A., Graduate School of Medicine, University of Pennsylvania, Philadelphia, Pa.

*Girard, Dr. Rene, Warner-Chilcott Laboratories, Research Division, Morris Plains, N. J.

*Gordon, Dr. H. A., Lobund Institute, Notre Dame, Ind.

Gottschalk, Dr. C. W., Department of Medicine, University of North Carolina, Chapel Hill, N. C.

*Miller, Dr. Walter, University of Colorado School of Medicine, Denver, Colo.

Monroe, Dr. P. A. G., Department of Anatomy, University of Pennsylvania School of Medicine, Philadelphia 4, Pa.

*Moore, Dr. Dan H., Rockefeller Institute, York Ave. and 66th St., New York, N. Y.

Moreci, Dr. Anthony P., Division of Dermatology, Stanford University School of Medicine, Clay and Webster Streets, San Francisco, Calif.

*Mossman, Dr. H. W., Department of Anatomy, University of Wisconsin Bardeen Laboratories, Madison, Wis.

*Myers, Dr. Hugh J., School of Dentistry, University of Kansas City, Kansas City, Mo.

Nace, Dr. Paul Foley, Department of Biology, McMaster University, Hamilton, Ontario, Canada

Nicoll, Dr. Paul A., Department of Physiology, Indiana University, Bloomington, Ind.

Ogden, Dr. E., 1730 Arlington Ave., Columbus 12, Ohio.

*Orsini, Dr. Margaret, Department of Anatomy, University of Wisconsin, Madison, Wis.

*Oyen, Dr. Fritz, Dow Chemical Company, Midland, Mich.

Padawer, Dr. Jaques, Department of Biochemistry, Albert Einstein College of Medicine, Eastchester Rd. and Morris Park Ave., New York 61, N. Y.

Page, Dr. Irvine H., Research Division, Cleveland Clinic, Cleveland 6, Ohio

Palade, G. E., Rockefeller Institute of Medical Research, York Ave. and 66th St., New York, N. Y.

Parpart, Dr. Arthur K., Department of Biology, Princeton University, Princeton, N. J.

*Peck, Dr. Harold M., Merck Institute, West Point, Pa.

*Perlman, Dr. Henry B., Department of Surgery, University of Chicago, Chicago 37, Ill.

Peterson, Dr. Lyle H., Department of Physiology, University of Pennsylvania Medical School, Philadelphia 4, Pa.

Ramsey, Dr. Elizabeth M., Department of Embryology, Carnegie Institute of Washington, Baltimore 5, Wash.

*Rappaport, Dr. A. M., Department of Physiology, University of Toronto, 134 Clements Ave., Toronto, Ontario, Canada

*Rebert, Dr. Richard R., 4545 Oleata Ave., St. Louis 16, Mo.

*Renkin, Dr. Eugene, Department of Physiology, George Washington University School of Medicine, 1335 W St., Washington 5, D.C.

*Reynolds, Dr. S. R. M., University of Illinois College of Medicine, 1853 West Polk St., Chicago 12, Ill.

*Rodbard, Dr. S., University of Buffalo, Buffalo, N. Y.

Roofe, Dr. Paul G., Department of Anatomy, University of Kansas School of Medicine, Lawrence, Kan.

*Sadow, Dr. H. S., U. S. Vitamin Corp., 250 East 43rd St., New York 17, N. Y.

Samuels, Dr. Saul S., Editor, *Angiology,* 151 East 83rd St., New York 28, N. Y.

*Sanders, Dr. A. G., Dunn School of Pathology, Oxford University, South Parks Road, Oxford, England

*Sapirstein, Dr. Leo, Department of Physiology, Ohio State University, Columbus, Ohio

Saunders, Dr. B. L. de C. H., Department of Anatomy, Dalhousie University, Halifax, Nova Scotia, Canada

*Savlov, Dr. Edwin D., University of Rochester School of Medicine, Department of Surgery, Rochester, N. Y.

*Schlegel, Dr. Jørgen U., Urological Research Laboratory, University of Rochester, Strong Memorial Hospital, Rochester 20, N. Y.

Shapiro, Dr. John L., Vanderbilt University Hospital, Nashville, Tenn.

Slechta, Dr. Robert, Department of Biology, Boston University, Boston 15, Mass.

Sloan, Dr. Margaret H., National Research Council, 2101 Constitution Ave., Washington 25, D.C.

*Smith, Dr. Catherine A., Washington University Medical School, St. Louis 10, Mo.

Smith, Dr. Christianna, Department of Zoology, Mount Holyoke College, South Hadley, Mass.

Smith, Dr. Douglas F., Argonne National Laboratory, Box 299, Lemont, Ill.

*Snook, Dr. Theodore, University of North Dakota, School of Medicine, Department of Anatomy, Grand Forks, N. D.

Stahlman, Dr. Mildred, Vanderbilt University Hospital, Nashville, Tenn.

Stavitzky, Dr. A. B., 607 Willow Drive, Euclid 32, Ohio

*Steer, Dr. Arthur, Lt. Col., Walter Reed Army Institute of Research, Walter Reed Army Medical Center, Washington 12, D.C.

Steinetz, Dr. Bernard G., Department of Physiology, Warner-Chilcott Laboratories, Morris Plains, N. J.

Still, Dr. G. W., Department of Physiology, George Washington University School of Medicine, 1335 H Street, Washington 5, D.C.

*Stoughton, Dr. R. B., Western Reserve University, 2065 Adelbert Rd., Cleveland 6, Ohio

*Sudak, Dr. Frederick N., Albert Einstein College of Medicine, Eastchester Rd. and Morris Park Ave., New York 61, N. Y.

*Swain, Dr. William M., National Drug Company, Philadelphia, Pa.

Tischendorf, Dr. Friedrich, Anatomisches Institut, Universitaedt, Cologne, Germany

*Todd, Dr. I. A. D., Toronto University, Toronto, Ontario, Canada

Valdivia, Dr. Enrique, Department of Pathology, University of Wisconsin, Madison 6, Wis.

Wakerlin, Dr. G. E., American Heart Association, Inc., New York, N. Y.

Walter, Dr. J. B., Royal College of Surgeons, Lincoln's Inn Fields, London W.C. 2, England

*Warner, Dr. Ben W., School of Dentistry, University of Kansas City, Kansas City, Mo.

*Warner, Dr. Louise, Department of Anatomy, Georgetown University School of Medicine, Washington, D.C.

*Warner, Dr. Nancy E., Department of Pathology, University of Chicago, Chicago 37, Ill.

Webb, Dr. Richard L., Department of Anatomy, Indiana University School of Medicine, Bloomington, Ind.

Weisiger, Dr. James R., Division of Medical Sciences, National Research Council, Washington, D.C.

Weston, Dr. J. K., Parke Davis & Co., Detroit, Mich.

*Wiedeman, Dr. Mary P., Department of Physiology, Temple University School of Medicine, Philadelphia 40, Pa.

Williams, Dr. Roy G., Department of Anatomy, University of Pennsylvania, Philadelphia 4, Pa.

*Willson, Dr. John T., 3079 South Cherry Way, Denver, Colo.

Wilson, Dr. Armine T., Chief, Bacteriology, Alfred Du Pont Institute, Wilmington, Del.

*Wilson, Dr. J. Walter, Department of Biology, Brown University, Providence 12, R. I.

Wood, Dr. Sumner, New England Deaconess Hospital, Boston 15, Mass.

*Worthington, Dr. W. Curtis, Jr., 17 Morton Ave., Westwood, Charleston, S. C.

Wyman, Dr. Leland C., Department of Biology, Boston University, Boston 15, Mass.

Yeager, Dr. J. Franklin, National Heart Institute, Bethesda 14, Md.

Yerganian, Dr. George, Children's Cancer Research Foundation, 15 Binney St., Boston, Mass.

*Yevich, Dr. Paul P., Pathology Branch, Chemical Corps Medical Laboratories, Army Medical Center, Md.

*Zweifach, Dr. B. W., Department of Pathology, New York University–Bellevue Medical Center, 550 First Ave., New York 16, N. Y.

Financial assistance from the following agencies and firms is gratefully acknowledged.

  The United States Public Health Service (Grant H-2662)

  Abbott Laboratories

  Ciba Pharmaceutical Products, Inc.

  Lakeside Laboratories, Inc.

  Eli Lilly & Company

  Merck Institute for Therapeutic Research

  National Drug Company

  Schering Foundation, Inc.

  G. D. Searle & Company

  Smith, Kline & French Laboratories

  Sterling-Winthrop Research Laboratories

  Warner-Chilcott Laboratories

  Wellcome Research Laboratories

INDEX